Let Hope In

Let Hope In

My Journey with Pancreatic Cancer

Roger Whitaker

Cathy Whitaker

Roger Whitaker

CONTENTS

CONTENTS

CONTENTS

Forward by Rick Whitaker

Let Hope In is Roger's open and transparent journey of living life in the grips of probable death.

Cathy, Rick, and Roger

As a pastor, I have walked with many who have entered a life that includes cancer. My desire was to love and encourage them with hope from the One who created them. I would also share with them what I hope to learn from their personal journey. Who is exempt from the possibility of walking on their road, including me... and you? I knew their physical and emotional experiences would benefit me if I too entered this life. Also, from what I have learned, I knew I could better love, encourage, and serve others who will eventually hear the words, "you have cancer".

My journey with Roger was very personal. He is my brother. He was born in 1947, and I was born in 1951. As his younger brother, and only sibling, I have watched and learned from him my entire life. When he shared he was diagnosed with pancreatic cancer, my mind immediately reviewed others I had known with pancreatic cancer. My thoughts and experiences were that it statistically was a fast death sentence. Against this backdrop, my wife Cathy, and I felt compelled to move from Seattle, Washington to Owasso, Oklahoma and be close during his journey with cancer.

Being up close and personal, we have learned so many things. His approach to his disease was realistic, determined to beat it, planned toward the future beyond cancer, and his faith was his foundation. You will see that Roger has a unique gift of allegory as he writes to express his emotions.

Let Hope In is a compilation of his life-journey through social media, group text, and emails with the intent to encourage his family and friends. Consequently, many who didn't know Roger began to follow his posts. Even today, we don't know who was most blessed in his journey. His followers were always reaching out to Roger to love and encourage him, while most indicated he was blessing them daily. No doubt, you will be encouraged by reading *Let Hope In*.

I don't know what is motivating you to read Roger's book. You may be a family member, a good friend, or someone who has just been diagnosed with cancer. You may also be someone who has lost a friend or family member to cancer. You will discover Roger knows your heart and desires to give you hope in your journey.

2

I Have Cancer

We have all faced a difficult situation in our lives at some point in time. It could be something that we had to face ourselves or something we had to face with a loved one or friend.

I am writing this book for those facing one of those difficult situations in their lives and not sure where to turn for help. You could be the person facing the unknown or you could be a parent, relative, friend, sibling, child, or a caregiver that wants to help but doesn't know how to either.

In July 2022, I was faced with the news I had Pancreatic cancer. All I knew was this was not good news, and I had no prior knowledge or experience in how to navigate this turn in the road. My life was about to change, but how? Would I have the courage to stand firm and face a life-threatening situation? In my case, the challenge was going to be fighting cancer. Maybe in your life, it is something totally different.

My book, "Let Hope In" is the story of my journey facing pancreatic cancer. There were a lot of unknowns at the start. It was not easy and there were tough days. Somedays, I just wanted to give up. But, I couldn't. Hope was the driving force that let me take one step at a time while reminding me to forget the odds. I learned to be patient along the roller coaster ride of emotions and those unknown twists and turns around each corner.

Sometimes the odds are totally against us, and it does not appear there is much hope. I want you to know, until the game is over and there are no outs left, there is hope. Find within yourself the courage and determination to never allow yourself to quit. You will be tested to give up, but face each hour and each day with your strong will and determination to keep moving forward. Know that you are not alone, but there are people that care about you and are pulling for you.

We all have the choice of how we face our challenges and adversity in our lives. I want to encourage you to not give up no matter how dark and stormy the clouds are around you. Keep hope and positive thoughts in your life. There is a saying I really enjoy reading each day. It says, "One small positive thought in the morning can change your whole day". Believe that one day that shining light will penetrate the darkness and turn the sky bright again.

I will never forget that day in July 2022 when the doctor entered my hospital room and gave me the test results

of my scans and MRI's. It was a sunny, hot, and steamy day outside, but inside that hospital room dark clouds were forming. I was told I had a cancerous mass on my pancreas. At that moment, I knew my world was changing.

I have the big "C". I have cancer! What does the world of having cancer look like? My head was swirling. What do I do? Where do I begin? The internet told me I did not have much of a chance to survive.

I have always been one to face my challenges head on, and I knew cancer was a killer, but people can get cured and live a long and healthy life. Right? So, I had to decide. I could either just grit my teeth and wait for the cancer to take my life or I could continue to hope and pray I would beat this thing. I decided to turn my illness over to God and trust Him to keep my hope and faith alive. I reminded myself that God said, "give Me your right hand and I will take care of you." I knew the power of God and that He could cure any illness. So, I decided to not let the cancer control my life, but rather, knowing I had Jesus in my life and in my corner, I would live my life the best I could while going through the process of surgeries and chemo treatments. This disease was not going to take away my will to fight. It was not going to drive me into a mental state of despair.

As I write "Let Hope In" I want to share with you the things I had to learn. My questions began with, what is it like having cancer and having chemo treatments and surgery? How might my life and my family be affected? How do I cope and muster the energy to not give up?

When all seems lost and you think this is the end, pick yourself up off the ground and fight for your life. Many things may be out of your control, but I believe how you face challenges is one thing you can control. Ask God to lead you along this journey. You can beat this adversity. Call upon your faith and believe in the power of prayer. Call upon your family and friends to stand with you and trust your doctors and nurses. Hold tightly to God's hand, and always believe in yourself and never let go of hope.

When I heard I had cancer, I started thinking this could be the end of my life. In my case, being diagnosed with cancer was bad enough, but to have pancreatic cancer, well let's just say, I didn't know of anyone that had survived this disease. I was in a battle for my life. However, let me be clear, other than my faith in God, believing in the power of prayer, my trust in my doctors and nurses, and my will to push forward, I did not have any control over curing my cancer. I had no control over my fate. My fate was in the hands of God and those He chose to use their skills and prayers to heal me.

You might be thinking it's easy for me to write this book because I have survived cancer and I'm writing about it after the fact. Therefore, I have a happy ending. Well, quite the contrary. I am still in the early phases of beating cancer. The most difficult phases of chemo treatments, and the Whipple surgery are behind me, but I am just a few months into the first two years of having my first two scans come back cancer free. The next two years are my most critical years and the higher odds of the cancer returning. After that, the odds will begin to turn in my favor of living a normal life. So, I am still struggling to beat pancreatic cancer. Nothing has changed in my will to be cured.

This will sound strange, but I feel blessed that I must travel this road. I have received and continue to receive infinite blessings from my experiences, and I want to share those with you. Then, you will see why I am able to be here writing a book today. But most of all, I want my experience to motivate you to stay strong as you travel difficult periods in your life.

It was difficult knowing I had cancer and it raised doubts in my mind about living much longer. I remember getting home from the hospital and facing the reality my world was coming apart. I have always wondered if I would want to know when I was going to die or rather not know. As I was sitting thinking about it, tears were forming in my eyes. I now felt like I knew when I was going to die. But, then, I started thinking about all the people supporting and praying for me and my will to fight to the end. I then told myself I could follow this path laid out before me. I can do this!

I did not get much sleep my first night at home. Each morning I spent a few minutes reading a book of spiritual thoughts for the day along with scriptures from the Bible. In the early morning hours, I pulled out my devotional book, and this is what I read. God said....."Hold out your right hand and I will take care of you." Wow! The tears were flowing so much now I could not read the rest of the devotion. How powerful is that to read on your first morning at home after finding out you have pancreatic cancer. God didn't say he was going to heal me, but He was going to take care of me. From that point forward, I was at peace with my future treatments and the outcome, whatever it would be. I was not going to fight this battle alone. I was going to trust God and give it my best shot. I had my faith in God on my side. I had God holding my right hand and walking with me.

After help and a recommendation from a well-connected friend, I found my oncologist and surgeon. They are the best. There are not words to adequately express my appreciation to my Oncologist, Dr. Scott Cole, his staff, and every person that works at Oklahoma Cancer Specialists and Ressearch Institute; my surgeon, Dr. Edward Cho, at the University of Oklahoma Health Sciences Center and his staff; my family and the hundreds of friends praying and visiting me. I had countless amazing people, including churches and people I did not know, praying and supporting me. They made the difference. I had given them my complete trust. I now had countless friends and untold numbers of people who elected to give their professional careers to the cause of beating cancer standing with me. I was reminded I was not going to take this journey alone.

At the request of family and friends supporting me and praying for my healing, I decided to document my story so they and others could follow my progress and hopefully understand the process of treating cancer. Writing my journal entries was great therapy for me as well. However, what surprised me was the response from those that were following my story. They encouraged me to continue writing and thanked me for sharing my journey with them. Several were going through cancer treatments and were inspired by my experiences. I was energized by the continuous responses of encouragement. We were feeding off each other. The followers of my journey grew each day. The number of people that cared and prayed was amazing.

Each chapter of this book begins with the actual journal entry I recorded on that specific date. I have also put the original journal entries in italics.

I want to be very clear about this path I am traveling. Although I am the one living this journey, I don't want it to be about me. I want my adventure to be about the power of prayer and support that continues to be delivered from my family and friends. I want it to be about the doctors and nurses that give their lives to help people with cancer. Most importantly, I want it to be about the power of prayer and works of God that heal when so many are praying for healing. I am just an ordinary guy that had cancer and happens to be the main character in an amazing and humbling experience.

I have played sports my entire life, starting at 6 years old. Sports taught me the importance of relying on a team to win the game. It has taught me how to compete on the field of competition and to never quit in the face of adversity and learn what it takes to win. Baseball was my love and allowed me to get my college paid for and compete at the highest level of college competition. I played for the University of Tulsa, and we finished 2nd in 1969 and third in 1971 of the College World Series. The university athletic department, and especially the alumni athletes at TU, have played a huge role in keeping my spirits up. They know what it takes to win and beat adversity. I can't thank them enough.

Another source of support came from close friends that have had cancer in the past.

Larry and Suzi have been friends since we were young kids. Larry was also a teammate on the University of Tulsa baseball team. They both have undergone numerous surgeries that should have taken their lives. Suzi also had Dr. Cole as her oncologist and loved him as much as I. She was a great resource for what to expect, but most importantly watching them both handle their treatments with such positive attitudes inspired me.

Larry and Suzi after Larry had just been inducted into the Tulsa McLain Hall of Fame

Roger and Jan

Roger and Jan are great friends. He is another of my former baseball teammates at the University of Tulsa. A few years ago, they experienced a very difficult tragedy.

They raised three beautiful daughters, Andi, Sarah, and Laura. Sarah had a passion to help others and especially young kids. She joined an organization that had ministry opportunities in Africa. While serving in Africa, she and several of her co-workers attended a conference several miles away. On their way back home, they had a car accident that took the life of Sarah. She was 32 years old and living out her passion with a loving and caring heart. Of course, Roger and Jan were heartbroken to receive the news they had lost one of their daughters. While giving them my support and trying to help in any way I could, I witnessed firsthand how they stayed strong through this period in their lives. They leaned on God and their friends for support knowing Sarah was living her dream and was very much loved by the people she was helping. I admired them for how they handled this tragedy.

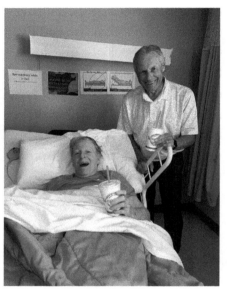

Brian and me enjoying our chocolate shakes

Another person that I get inspired by every time I visit him is Brian. Brian had a stroke a couple years ago which paralyzed his right side. He is now confined to a bed. He was a great baseball player at TU as well and a good friend. Each time I go visit Brian I leave feeling totally inspired by him. I could not do what he is doing with such a good spirit. When he found out I had cancer, tears came to his eyes. He was very concerned about me. He often prays for me before I leave. Here is a guy that is confined to a bed for the rest of his life, and he is praying for me. Amazing! I love taking him his favorite chocolate shake occasionally as a surprise treat. He really lights up when he gets that first taste. Something we take for granted is such a huge treat for him.

Alicia-Connor Todd and her husband Jackson have been great friends the last several years. Jackson is a former major league baseball pitcher and Alicia is an RN MSN. Alicia has been a champion for my cause and being a nurse always gave me the medical view and encouragement as she walked with me on my journey. Alicia and Jackson were always looking out for me to ensure I had everything I needed, including meals delivered to my house.

In my Facebook updates I use several examples from my sports experiences and others I have lived, and in some cases imagined. One fault I have, if you ask me a simple question, you are going to get a long-winded story as your answer. A storyteller must be hidden somewhere in my soul. Where do the words come from? I have no idea. I guess I just like to ramble and sometimes my mind just goes off into a creative story telling direction. Hence, you will notice later in the book my journal entries usually turned into a story. You will also notice I use a lot of baseball analogies as well.

Jackson and Alicia

So, I give credit for my progress each step of the way to God and my faith in him; to my doctors and nurses that have given their lives to helping people like me that have a disease that kills; and to my family, close friends, and followers who never lost the faith and encouraged me to keep my hope alive.

3

Finding the Cancer - Planning for the Journey

Fly fishing the San Juan River in New Mexico

In 2022, I was a healthy and active 75-year-old male. I played golf, fly-fished the streams, worked out, traveled, and did anything I wanted to do. I had a personal trainer and worked out with him three times a week. Late May and into June, I found myself struggling to finish my drills. Rather than feeling refreshed like I normally do after a workout, I was feeling tired and couldn't finish.

Then in June 2022, I experienced a weeklong bout with stomach issues constantly and my urine turned dark orange. Knowing this did not look right, I called my primary care physician. He told me to go to the emergency room and have them run tests. After a few tests results came back, the ER doctor said he wanted to check me into the hospital and run a few other tests the next day. Unfortunately, there were no rooms available in the main hospital and I was placed on an ER bed. I was in a small exam room that had a lot of commotion going on outside my door. I did not get any rest that night. Was I concerned about the upcoming tests? No, just glad someone was going to find out what was wrong with me. The ER doctor did not seem overly concerned or anxious, therefore neither did I. Just routine tests the next day. Right?

The tests the next day showed a blockage in my biliary duct going to my pancreas. This was why I was seeing outward signs of something not right. The doctors thought the duct was obstructed from the inside and put in a stent. However, a mass was detected growing on the outside of the duct forcing it to close. The mass was cancerous. If the mass had not caused some sort of outward sign of something wrong with my body, it would have continued to grow, and my story would be very short. As it was, the doctors were able to catch the cancer at stage 1A level. This meant the cancer was discovered in the early stages and had not spread yet. At least that was the prognosis.

I was then referred to an Oncologist, Dr. Scott Cole, who laid out a plan for me. In our initial discussions I made it clear to Dr. Cole and later to my surgeon, Dr. Edward Cho, that I wanted straightforward and honest discussions. If the news was bad, then I wanted to hear the bad news. They agreed this is how they wanted to proceed as well. In addition to finding the cancer in an early stage, the second good news was that it appeared I would be a candidate for the extensive and com-plicated Whipple surgery. This was the only chance of saving my life. It is difficult finding doctors who have performed this surgery often. With this surgery, you want someone who has performed several because it is one of the most difficult and complex surgeries you can have. It can take 8 to 10 hours to perform the surgery.

We talked through several scenarios, but Dr. Cole put together a plan to perform four chemo treatments before the surgery and many more after. The mass was too close to the aorta, so the hope was the chemo would shrink the cancer enough to give the surgeon more room to operate on the mass with less chance of nicking the aorta. The only time I was anxious was my initial meeting with Dr. Cho. He was going to tell me if I was a candidate for the Whipple surgery. With the complexity and length of the surgery, and at my age and the position and possible spread of the cancer, it made my qualifications for surgery tenuous. I was quite relieved when he told me it was a go. Here again, all the odds, even with a successful surgery, were not promising.

I had prostate cancer in 2010, so I was somewhat familiar with having cancer. But nothing like what I was going to face over several months and probably a few years. With prostate cancer, the cancer was confined to the prostate, and I elected to remove the prostate so that I would not have to deal with radiation or frequent checkups the rest of my life. Other than surgical hernias that developed several months later, the surgery was easy and removed any possibility the cancer would return by escaping my prostate. My advice to every male over the age of 55, get regular prostate checkups. It can be a killer if you let it progress outside the prostate. I had a friend that died from prostate cancer because he refused to go to the doctor.

The family at mom's funeral service. The back row...Ali, Ryan, Brock, Cathleen and Barbe.

The first order of business when I was sure I had pancreatic cancer, was to discuss with my wife how we were going to tell the kids and what role we wanted them to play. I have a son, Ryan, and daughters Barbe and Cathleen.

How do we tell them and how much do we share? How involved should they be with decisions and attending doctor's appointments. Part of the problem at the time was you were only allowed to have two people in the room with the doctor. The rooms were not big enough for several people to attend. This applied to chemo treatments as well. The other problem was with more people involved in the decision process; it made it harder to come to a consensus. I love my kids, but they all had their own perspectives on where, who, and how cancer should be treated. I had mine as well. We had several open, frank, and honest discussions about where I should get the treatments, who should perform the surgery and getting buy-in on the final decision. Each of the kids was valuable and needed along the journey. My wife was also helping her mom during this time with a bout in the hospital. Her family really helped by traveling from Florida, Colorado, California, Kansas, and Hawaii to help with my care and give my wife support with her mom. They all were great. Ryan, Barbe and Cathleen played valuable roles as well. Cathleen is the researcher of the family. She is very good at it and would talk to the doctors in their language just from her research on the internet and talking with her surgeon cousin David. I was not interested in reading anything on the internet, except the Whipple surgery. I found it too demoralizing to read all the information. I knew my odds and they weren't good. I let my wife and Cathleen do the research and tell me what I should know. They were my sources of information. I just couldn't do it yet.

We have doctors in the family and doctors that are friends. When the first diagnosis of pancreatic cancer was received, most of the professionals said I must go to Mayo or MD Anderson clinics. I did not disagree with this assessment, however, I wanted to meet my doctors first. I also knew the frequent visits and month-long treatments would be difficult and put a strain on my wife and me in either staying somewhere like Houston or Minneapolis. Plus, I had a desire to remain at home in Tulsa. Especially if something went wrong, I wanted to be home and close to family and friends. However, this was my personal criteria. I would highly recommend that both Mayo and MD Anderson be high on your list for possible treatments.

After meeting Dr. Cole and Dr. Cho, I really liked them and their plan of action for me. Hence, under some protest from the family, I made my decision to remain in Tulsa for my treatment. After the kids were able to meet both doctors, they too were impressed and liked the doctors as well as the facility where I would be treated. We had a unanimous buy-in.

The kids had lots of questions that I could not answer until I talked to my doctors. The initial discussion centered around how much I should share with them. Should I share with them each step of the process, including the bad news and frequent bouts of chemo treatments I would be faced with? They are all grown adults and wanted to know everything, the good along with the bad. I told them this would be a difficult journey and there would be moments of raw emotions and a roller coaster ride with turns and twists. But I also told them I wanted them to be part of the journey and not just followers watching from the outside. I wanted them to speak freely and openly about whatever was on their mind. I needed their opinions and help. I knew they would be reading the internet and easily find anything they want to know about pancreatic cancer. So, I would rather we talk and discuss what the doctors were saying and what I was going through rather than trusting everything on the internet. Don't get me wrong, there is very useful data on the internet, but it can be a source of getting too much information and not getting the full context of what you are reading. It can be very depressing, and it can suck the positive outlook out of your body. I would suggest you not depend on the internet as your only source of information.

Next, I told my 95-year-old mom and my brother Rick and my sister-in-law, Cathy. I loved my mom's faith in God. She was fearful at first for one of her sons. She knew the killing nature of cancer after having lost her mother and brother to cancer. She was not about to lose a son as well. Rick and Cathy are also very strong in their faith.

Rick is an ordained minister and Cathy has been ministering to others in need for years. They both knew the severity of the cancer and what the possible outcome could be. They wanted to know what they could do to help me. At the time they were living in Seattle, Washington, which is several hundred miles from Owasso, Oklahoma. My first request to them was to help take care of the information flow to mom and roller coaster ride we would be traveling. Mom wanted to know all the little details of what I was going

Mom at 95 years old received an honor for 32 years of service in the retirement center

through each day. She wanted to be sure I was ok. Mom dreaded hearing any bad news or that I was ill from the chemo treatments. She would call several times each day to check up on me. Bless her soul, it seemed like I was giving her hourly updates. She could tell from my voice if I was having a bad or good moment; a great day or a bad day. I will never forget after one of our phone conversations, mom forgot to hang up the phone. I listened for a little bit and then, I heard her praying and thanking God because I sounded good. All she wanted was for me to feel good. This made tears well up in my eyes and they started running down my cheeks. Wow, she was always looking for the positive moments.

When I told mom I was going to have chemo treatments before surgery, she always said the cancer would be gone and they would not need to operate. There was no other option. The cancer would be gone!

I tried to manage her expectations but didn't want to dampen her positive spirit and prayers for full recovery.

I wish I had the faith of my mom. I knew God could perform miracles, but in my worldly view, I knew I had some major things to go through before the cancer could be treated, let alone be removed.

I could write a chapter on Rick and Cathy. They have been the pillars during my entire ordeal. They moved temporarily to Tulsa to help me in any way they could, but mostly helping mom while one of her sons was suffering with cancer. None of us could see how circumstances would change so suddenly and how having them nearby would be so important. It was a God thing for them to come to Tulsa. More on this later.

Rick and Cathy

The next order of business was who and how to tell our friends. Should I even share with anyone I had cancer? I did not want sympathy. But I did have several friends that would want an update. I decided to use a couple of methods of communicating my progress. First, I had a private baseball Facebook page several of us old baseball guys and their families used to stay in touch. This would be the main channel. Several friends do not use Facebook, so I chose to update them through email. I had over 150 email users and over 250 Facebook users that would get the same message. As my journals became more public, the members on each platform grew each week. What began as an update on my progress, turned into a therapy session for me, but also something several people were encouraging me to continue. They even started sharing my journals with other friends. Before I knew it, I had churches and many people I did not know following my progress. The prayers and support for my wellbeing were off the charts. When I had bad days, all I had to remember was all the people that had it worse than me, but especially all the people following my story and giving me encouragement. In addition to the doctors and nurses God gave the responsibility to heal me, I give as much credit to the people following my progress. God said if he heard the prayer request for my healing from two or more, he would honor their petitions for my healing. I had requests for my healing from more than I could count. This is what gave me the infinite blessings I will forever remember.

I had a team of doctors, nurses, support from family and friends and a means of giving frequent updates on my condition. I felt now, it was just a matter of executing the plan. God had given me peace in my mind and heart. I was in a good place and ready for the battle to begin. I had a large army beside me and it grew every day. I was really blessed. God had my right hand, and my followers had my left hand. How powerful and humbling is that? Now you see why I say I was blessed every step of the way. Everything that would happen going forward I could trust it would be the "will of the Father". When I was 9 years old, I turned my life over to Jesus and committed to follow Him. Now at 75 years old, I still choose to trust God daily. He gave me peace. I felt like I was in a win-win situation. I no longer feared death, because I would either be in heaven or continue to live on this earth with my family and friends.

My journey was ready to begin. On July 3, 2022, I entered my first post on Facebook. In the next several chapters of my journal entries, I will be sharing my experiences of going through the process of treating cancer.

4 ▌

Journal Entry July 3, 2022 - The Journey Begins

Journal Entry July 3, 2022

Being in the hospital this week, I have had a lot of time reflecting on and recognizing how lucky I am to have such wonderful friends. Your prayers and concerns for my well-being are just "very special". We have had several opportunities to share our prayers and concerns for each other, but this time I was on the receiving end. You have no idea how comforting that is. All I can say in inadequate terms, is "Thank You". The phone calls, texts, emails, voicemails, visits to the hospital and at home are an amazing testimony of the quality and caring hearts each of you have for others. It is obvious.

After a few calls, visits, etc. while in the hospital, the nurses asked me if I was someone special. "You have a lot of friends." All I could say back was, I am just "one of the guys." They are the special ones!"

To put it in perspective, when I need a "shot of inspiration", I go to visit our friend, Brian Humphrey. He just always makes me feel better. I got home from the hospital Friday afternoon, so Saturday morning, I am tired and a little sore from the surgery. I need to go see Brian. I walk into his room, where he is always laying in his bed. He looks over and notices me coming in the door and begins to smile. I tell Brian, I am sorry I didn't get to come by this week because I was in the hospital for some minor surgery. His eyes widen and a little tear starts forming in the corner of his eye. "Are you ok, Buddy? I am concerned for you." Are you kidding me? He is lying in bed, paralyzed on the right side and he is shedding a tear for me! "I am fine Brian, but I have to go back to the hospital next week for a second surgery, but I am fine." He seems content with that and then says, "we still going to the Driller game?" "Absolutely, Brian, we are going to the Driller game and if we can stay awake, we are going to watch the fireworks after the game. I think some of the guys may be there too." He lights up with his big grin and gives me a fist bump. I got a double shot of inspiration this Saturday morning.

I tell you this story because he is probably in the worst condition of all of us, but still has such a positive influence on others. In your own ways, you do the same thing, whether you recognize it or not. I know because I have received it from you as well.

Me, Brian and my great friend Roger at the TU Women's Softball game

Next Thursday, I will be going back for a similar surgery, where they will run a tube down my throat to the mass on my pancreas and take a biopsy and do some snooping around looking at my pancreas and liver. It is an outpatient procedure. Then the following week, I will meet with the doctors and go over the results.

Thank you for your prayers and concerns, but mostly thank you for just being you! You are all very special people!

On the advice of my Primary Care physician, I went to the Emergency Room at Saint Francis South for tests to determine why I was not feeling well for several weeks. The initial tests raised enough questions in the doctor's analysis, it was determined I needed to be admitted to the hospital for additional tests. These tests revealed I had cancer.

I also had planned a baseball night out, in July, at the Tulsa Drillers double A baseball team with our former baseball players and families. I had arranged for Brian to attend the game as well. I will never forget how Brian just watched everything as we traveled to the game. He had not been out of his bed for several weeks. It was a joy watching his eyes light up just driving to the game. When we arrived at the game, he was greeted by over 60 former players and their families. What a great night for Brian. Since my energy level had decreased so much, I was given a wheelchair to help me get around at the game. So, Brian and I were wheelchair buddies.

The Driller organization arranged for all of us to go on the field after the 6th inning. Brian and I were escorted onto the field in our wheelchairs along with all the other players. Once we got to the field, I decided to stand with my grandkids, Georgie and Teddy.

Roger and Karen with me in my wheelchair at the Driller game

A great night at the Driller game with several of my former teammates

When they announced we were the former Tulsa University baseball players, we received a standing ovation. What a perfect recognition from our fans. Since discovering I had cancer a few days prior to the game, it was an emotional moment for me as well. The mind started swirling again. Would this be my last ball game and time with all the guys and their families? The raw emotional twists and turns of the journey were already beginning.

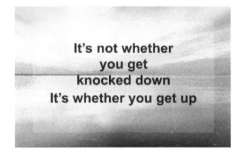

It's not whether you get knocked down It's whether you get up

5

Journal Entry July 7, 2022 - It's Getting Real

Journal Entry - July 7, 2022

Regarding my surgery....first, again, I cannot thank you enough for the amazing support you have given me. I am truly blessed.

I had the second surgery this morning where they examined my pancreas and liver. They confirmed that a large spot on my pancreas was cancer. However, based upon these initial results, it is operable, although a long and complex surgery. I consider this good news. I am feeling fine, but just taking a few off and on naps.

We will meet with the surgeon and oncologist next week to determine the next steps. Again, thank you for your support. You are awesome.

Up to this point, I don't think the reality of having cancer has been fully understood. I still had a second surgical procedure to be performed. This second surgery, much like the first surgery, would be running a scope down my throat to take a closer look at my pancreas and the large cancerous spot. This would determine the extent of the cancer and if it was operable. Of course, I was anxiously waiting for the doctor to give me the results. What if they can't operate? Does that confirm my limited knowledge that those with pancreatic cancer never survive? It was all so new to me that I did not understand the big picture yet. This would come very soon.

Was I in a panic doomsday mode? No. Surprisingly, I was still calm mentally. Physically, I was tired and wanted to take naps. I think the waiting game is the worst part because your mind starts thinking of all these different scenarios and "what ifs".

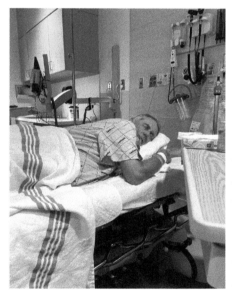

Waiting on the results from the surgical procedure checking out the mass on my pancreas. I was tired and just wanted to sleep.

The door opened and the doctor walked into the room and sat down in a chair next to my bed. I looked at his eyes and face but could not read his face to determine what he was about to tell me. So, he began to speak and give me the results of the scope. He says, "Yes, it is confirmed as we thought the spot on your pancreas is cancer. It appears we caught it early and does not show signs of spreading into other organs. However, we will not know until we do further scans and MRI's. The good news is that it is operable. We will send the results to your oncologist and surgeon, and they will put together a plan for your situation."

The report was good news and bad news. It was what I expected, but not what I wanted to hear. I was hoping the mass was not cancer. But on the other hand, it was caught early and operable. That was the best possible news for having pancreatic cancer. So, now I am a cancer patient. Yes, it is confirmed, I have cancer of the pancreas. So, it is time to get ready for my journey. I guess it had already started, and I did not realize it until now. No more "what if" scenarios. This is the reality.

My mind is now wondering what my journey would look like. Chemo treatments and surgery? I have heard chemo treatments are very difficult to take and have sickness type side effects. Surgery? I don't know what to expect but it does sound like lots of pain after the surgery. Having cancer was now the reality, but now I was wondering about how it is treated and if I can be cured. Is this the beginning of the end for me? It was not fear driving these thoughts, but more about the information I was starting to digest from Cathleen's research. I was now fully aware of the odds of survival.

In one of my morning devotions, God says in the Psalms, that "He broadens the path beneath me, so that my ankles will not turn. Do not focus too much on what is ahead of you, wondering whether you'll be able to cope with it. Only He knows what the future holds and what I am capable of."

I have been one to believe when obstacles are thrown at you, consider them opportunities to learn what you are capable of and to grow from them. But this was a big one that had big consequences. Can I do this? My competitive spirit says, "yes, I can." God says when tests and challenges come at you from all sides, consider it a joyful opportunity. I was already walking down a path that had unknowns around each corner. I would be tested in my will to never give up. But I was ready to begin. I would have to hold tightly to God's hand.

What was soon to happen was one of the most rewarding experiences in my life. I was really listening to God now because I had no control over my future. God said, "Call to me, and I will answer you, and show you great and mighty things, which you do not know." I was about to experience an amazing journey that was difficult but rewarding.

One day you will
tell your story
of how you have
overcome what
you are going through now,
and it will become
part of someone else's
survival guide.

6

Journal Entry July 9, 2022 - Hitting the Curve Ball

Journal Entry - July 9, 2022

Sorry everyone, I just had to share with you the wonderful day I had today. Of course, it is relative to what you consider a wonderful day.

Before I get into that, since I have had such overwhelming support from all of you, I want to give you an update on my health condition. I told you earlier the test results appeared to show signs of cancer on my pancreas. After several more rounds of tests this week, it is certain I have a 1-inch spot on my pancreas that is cancer. So, to address the elephant in the room, yes, I have pancreatic cancer. It is currently in stage 1B.

Because of your prayers and concerns for me, they have been answered by the fact it appears to be operable. At least that is the story today. So, thank you for those prayers. They are working! I am in the process of putting together what I consider some of the best doctors in this field together as a team to help me through this. This resulted in help from very high up sources that know who to call. I will be meeting with them this next week to put together the next steps of the process.

Yes, I have told my kids this will be a roller coaster ride with twists, turns, some up some down. So, hold on tight. But I did assure them, I would be a fighter until the end. That's just who I am. So, there, we can talk about it out loud. And by the way, if I write anything on this webpage and via email, I don't want this to be about me. There are a lot more people out there, even among us, that have gone through much worse things. Look at Brian Humphrey, who is bedridden the rest of his life. The guy that gives me inspiration each time I visit with him. Look at Larry and Suzi Byrd and their many years fighting cancer. Ken Knight and Steve Caves going through major heart conditions that should have killed them. And I could go on and on about each of you or family you have had to deal with tough times.

Sometimes life just doesn't seem fair. Well, let me tell you what I always tell my kids or the kids I am coaching. Life isn't fair, so be prepared to deal with those times when you think you are not being treated as you think you should. Life throws us curve balls. You must learn to hit the curve ball.

Now, that reminds me of the kidding I get from Phil Honeycutt. I think he was serious. "Whit, you could never hit the curve ball." What Phil doesn't understand. I was a contact hitter and only struck out three times. There is an art to hitting. BTW, Phil, I hit almost .350 each year in the leadoff spot,

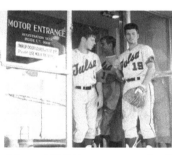

Me and Phil Honeycutt at the 1969
College World Series

which is supposed to get on base so you could get an rbi for bringing me home, which he did very well. You see Phil, I fouled off the curve balls, so I could work the pitcher into a hole that he had to bring me my pitch that I wanted to hit. It's all about working those curve balls to your favor and then they must bring the heater down the middle, which I was ready for. My pitch. Double in left center field. Hey, Phil, here I am standing on second base ready for you to bring me home!

Well, I may be getting a few life curve balls thrown my way right now. So, I will keep fouling them off until I get my pitch and the doctors can then do their thing. So, we aren't done yet. Keep those prayers coming. You have no idea how powerful they are.

Now, why was today such a great day? After what seems like endless cancer talk and trying to make the right decisions with my 95-year-old mom, my beautiful wife, my kids, Ryan, Barbe, Cathleen and my brother, Rick, and his wife Cathy, from Seattle, I finally said to Rick, I know it is 95 degrees outside, but I have to get out of the house and play some golf. I call a few guys to see if anyone is as crazy as I am, that might want to play as well. So, Gary Moutray and Steve Caves joined me and my brother for a round of golf. Then my dear friend, Ken Knight, said I don't want to play, but I do want to ride around with you. So, Ken rode around the course with us. Wow, Ken, thank you for that! We had fun playing and as the round was about to finish, I told my brother that I am so lucky to have so many friends that I play golf with, go fishing and just stay in touch with on Facebook and email. Then he told me something that really struck me. He said, "Roger, those aren't just friends that are here today, or that call you, or you visit with on Facebook, or played ball with. What you have are "foxhole friends". Think about that statement. He was right on! My friends aren't just friends, they are more than that! Everyone reading this little story of mine thinks what this label means to each of us. We are "foxhole friends"! Wow! Now that is special. That is why I keep saying each of you are amazing! Each of you is special.

Each of you are my "foxhole friends". That is why today was such a wonderful day! Thank you, my brother, Rick, for this astounding observation. Actions speak louder than words. Your actions have given a whole new meaning when I feel we are like brothers and sisters. We are more than that...."We are foxhole friends!" I love it so much; I just must keep saying those words.

So, in closing, I just had to share with you my revelation from today's outing. BTW....I will continue to foul off those curve balls to get my pitch! Again, thank you for being so special.

I am barely over one week into my journey. Where am I going? I have no idea. All I know is I will be meeting with my oncologist soon to get a better understanding of my cancer and how it will be treated. I am ready to meet my doctors and find out what I will be going through and what the doctors have to say about the chances of curing my cancer.

Using a baseball term, sometimes life sends us a curve ball. It can throw you off guard and of course, is usually unexpected. You may even think, why me? When I was coaching little league baseball and basketball while raising my kids, I would frequently hear the words, "that's not fair". Well, as I tried to teach them, yes, you are correct. Life isn't fair. Complaining about it or making excuses doesn't change a thing. Accept it and move on. You may have a boss that you don't like, or the kids bring home a bad grade and blame it on the teacher. Learn to deal with it. You cannot change the circumstance. The lesson to learn is how are you going to deal with it? Well, life threw me a curve ball when I got cancer. So, how am I going to deal with it? Feeling sorry for myself and asking "why me" doesn't help or change the outcome. At some point I must accept I just received one of life's curve balls.

What do you do if life throws you one of these curve balls? Depending on the nature of the circumstance, you can handle it yourself or if it is a big curve ball, then you may need additional help. As I stated earlier, curing cancer was totally out of my control. However, when my family and friends learned I had cancer, they rallied around me and gave me amazing support. This gave me comfort and peace, but most importantly, it energized me to give everything I had to face my situation head on.

Tom Jenkins, me, Ken Knight and Roger Adams playing golf in Maui, Hawaii

I had been dealing with the knowledge I had cancer and discussing it with my family. It would never leave my mind. I needed to get out of the house and clear my mind for a few hours at least. I told my brother, it doesn't matter how hot it is, let's go play golf. Gary, Steve and Ken joined Rick and me for a round of golf. We had a great time on the course. It doesn't matter what score we shot; we just love the camaraderie of the guys getting together.

When Rick defined my friends as "foxhole friends", I was astounded by how he defined them. I had never thought of it that way. But he was right. It was the highest compliment I could think of to describe my friends. Wow! Just think what that means. As I walked the path of the next several months, the actions of my friends proved my new favorite words, "foxhole friends".

7

Journal Entry July 15, 2022 - It Is What It Is

Journal Entry July 15, 2022

Good Friday morning to everyone. I am up early this morning for another small procedure. But first, let me bring you up to date on my health condition. I won't bore you with too many stories for the next few months, but I met with my doctor Thursday morning about my condition and what is next.

My wife and I are extremely pleased with the great team of doctors being organized. The leader of the team is Doctor Scott Cole, from the Oklahoma Cancer Specialists and Research Institute.

Dr. Cole spent about an hour going over my test results and explained my condition and options going forward using pictures showing me the location of my cancer, and why it is in a difficult position and the reason for our first step of the journey. It is sitting at the head of the pancreas, which is good news and is Stage 1, which also is good news. However, there are all kinds of blood vessels, including the aorta, lymph nodes, and several body parts together in this area. He said I will need the Whipple surgery, which is a very long, 6–12-hour surgery, to remove the cancer. We are going to start with Chemotherapy treatments for a couple months and try to shrink the tumor away from the aorta and get any other cancer cells that are not visible. He said I only get one shot with the Whipple surgery, and this will give me the best odds for the surgeon to be successful.

So, this morning I am headed to the clinic to implant the chemo port in my chest so we can start the chemo treatments. The journey has begun. But my motto is, "it is what it is". I really feel good about the journey even though it will be rough at times, but as my old friend Tom Maxwell told me yesterday, "I feel good about this, because us old ball players are tough". I agree with Tom, I feel good about the result, and I am an old tough ball player and even if I am old, I still have a lot of fight in me!

So, keep those prayers coming. I truly believe you have made a difference so far. I will share this story, surprise, another story. But this is a cool story. As you know, I have a lot of faith in my God. The morning after I found out I had cancer, I opened my devotional book, and the very first sentence, it said, God speaking....."give me your right hand and I will help you". That was all I needed to hear. My kids were concerned and scared as well, but I told them my story and said, "Let's do this journey together and you hold my left hand. We are going to beat this thing because I have so many amazing "foxhole friends" praying for me and God holding my right hand. He's got this.

The Whipple surgery is a very tough surgery, so this time, I am going to have to hit this curve ball for an extra base hit. I keep seeing this vision, approaching second base, and looking for Coach Shell for a signal to keep on coming to third. He is waving his arms to keep on coming. But this time I am thinking to myself as I am running to third

base. *I know Coach Shell is in heaven and I want to join him someday, but if he is waving me home, well, I love you Coach, but I think I will just stop at third base. Besides, Phil Honeycutt, Buckets, is coming up to plate later in the lineup. I will let Buckets knock me home later. I am not ready to score just yet. Still got a few more pitches left, and I am going to stand here at third base for a while.*

Sorry guys for the crazy stuff and stories that go through my head, (maybe I need brain surgery), but this is me and "it is what it is".

Life is full of difficult times, and we will go through some of these periods in our lives. I have been through many. How do we explain why we are having a tough period in our lives? How do I explain why I have cancer? Am I being punished by God for doing something that was unpleasing to him? Well, God doesn't work that way. He has said that He loves us and has forgiven us for our sins. However, because of our sins, there are bad things in the world in which we live in. Cancer and illness are some of those things we humans experience. Why do we want to blame God? It is not God's fault. So rather than trying to rationalize why I have cancer, I decided to accept the fact "it is what it is". For some reason, repeating these words take away the state of mind that I must know why. It also helps me accept the fact I have cancer and I don't worry about "why me?" So, the focus needs to be on moving forward on my journey and doing what my doctors tell me I need to do to get better.

I appreciated how my doctors would take their time and explain each step of the process. Up to this point, I was apprehensive about chemo treatments. All I knew was that they were not something I was looking forward to getting. But after the explanations from the doctors about the chemo treatments and the upcoming Whipple surgery, I was starting to understand what I needed to possibly cure the cancer, but also, what it would be like. I received a two-hour training session about chemo treatments, the different types of chemicals they would use, how it would be administered, how long each treatment would take and what side effects I should expect. I feel much better about the treatments now.

For those of you going through chemo treatments, you sit in a chair while they drip bags of chemo into your body through the port. There is no pain or discomfort during the process of administering the chemo. However, the side effects will hit you later. One of the best technical advances I experienced was getting a port implanted in my upper chest. Mine is still there and used when I go for my blood work. The port is implanted surgically in an operating room. It is round on one end, and a needle is placed inside one of your veins below your neck. It has never hurt, nor has it stopped me from doing anything, especially playing golf. Whenever you are giving blood for the labs or receiving your chemo chemicals, I call them my cocktail, they use the port rather than each time sticking a needle in the vein in your arm. I am so thankful for the port.

I knew I had to go through the chemo treatments before the Whipple surgery, but I also knew the chemo treatments would not remove the cancer from my pancreas. Whipple surgery was definite. So, the Whipple surgery was the only thing that would possibly remove the cancerous mass. The chemo treatments were shrinking the mass, but also killing any other cancer in my body that had not been visible.

The plan was coming together, and the steps of the process were being defined and explained in much detail. I knew some of the steps would be difficult and the journey would take several months. But "it is what it is."

8

Journal Entry July 20, 2022 - The Cookie

Journal Entry July 20, 2022

Hi everyone. I cannot thank you enough for the phone calls, cards, emails, texts, etc. You give me so much support. Here is my latest. I may not share a whole lot going forward, because we are starting the journey and there may not be much to report. I met with my surgeon this week that is doing the Whipple surgery. His name is Dr. Edward Cho. However, I have not eliminated Mayo or MD Anderson. But, I really like Dr. Cho and Dr. Scott Cole and the amount of experience they have with my cancer and the upcoming surgery. I know several of you have used these doctors, like Suzi Byrd and John Klahr, which also played into my decision and confidence. I met with my chemo nurse today wearing my TU facemask. She asked about what I did at TU, and I told her I was a "dirty old ball player". She said, "then you probably know John Klahr! He was my patient. We had a good time sharing the John Klahr story. Another reason I like these people.

So, on Tuesday of next week, I start chemo treatments at the Oklahoma Cancer Specialists and Research Institute. I will have treatments every other Tuesday for two months. Then, we will do a cat scan and move to the next step of Whipple surgery to remove the cancer. They said I could expect to lose 30-40 pounds, probably hair, etc. Maybe I will finally get back to my college baseball playing weight! After Whipple surgery, it will take 4-6 months to get back to my good healthy quality of life. I am hoping by Christmas. However, I am going to keep on doing everything I possibly can do; play golf, fish, and have lunch with my buddies, TU football and basketball games, etc.

The famous cookie. It was only one bite and the Cookie Monster made me eat it.

So, the journey has started and is getting real! Oh, about the picture of the cookie. Well, I was supposed to put my chemo port in last week. Since they put me under, I am not supposed to eat anything after midnight. Well, as I was leaving the house to go for the procedure, there was this cookie just sitting on the counter. The cookie monster on my shoulder said "Hey Whit, it's just a small cookie, so go for it. Well, I did." I am laying on the bed ready for my procedure and they said, "now you haven't eaten anything after midnight. Correct?" "Well, there was this cookie sitting on the counter, and the cookie monster said it was ok, since it was a small cookie." Wrong answer! We can't do the procedure and come back next week. So, tomorrow, my wife is vowing to tie my hands behind my back so I can't be tempted, we go again for the chemo port procedure." Darn cookie! Get away from me Satan, I mean Cookie Monster! Remove all cookies from my reach!

Sometimes during a difficult period in your life, there are light-hearted humorous moments. When I ate the cookie that derailed my procedure at the clinic, that was one of those funny moments. Maybe not at the time, but looking back it does bring a smile. When I went back the next week, all the nurses remembered the cookie incident and were laughing and asking what kind of cookie I could not resist. All I could say was the "Cookie Monster" made me do it. This time we were able to perform the surgery and implant the port in my chest.

As I was walking the path of my journey, I was still calm and not fearful of what was to come. The cookie incident did bring a smile to my face and created a fun moment. I was a little anxious about having bags of poison dripped into my body and what the side effects would be like. But, I was building confidence that maybe we could beat this cancer. Each time I was reminded of the odds that were against me. All we can do when we are in these situations is to keep faith and let hope drive us to keep pushing forward. I let hope in and recommitted myself to taking each day one at a time. There will be rough days ahead.

9

Journal Entry August 6, 2022 - One Pitch at a Time

Well, I have had so many of you reach out to me asking how I am doing with my journey to beat this pancreatic cancer, that I thought maybe I should give you an update. Before I do, I by no means want to be in the spotlight with this. I am a very lucky guy that has a chance to beat it. But there are so many of you that have gone through so much more and deserve our attention. I have mentioned before, the long struggles John Klahr, Suzi Byrd, Larry Byrd, and so many more have had to endure to get well, that mine is so insignificant. But, I can now relate to their journeys as I am moving along mine.

The journey and chemo treatments are not a fun experience as they can attest. I had one treatment two weeks ago and have my next cycle next Tuesday. The week after chemo is the down week and the second week you start feeling much better. Then you start thinking, dang, I must do this again in just a few more days. It can get depressing. I will probably have around 6-8 treatments before the Whipple surgery. But "it is what it is". You must keep on moving forward. Your calls, your texts, the meals, the cards, even videos from "Rudy".....you give the encouragement to keep the spirits up to fight and win this game. I cannot thank you enough.

However, I am learning a lot about myself too. My new word I am learning to apply to myself is "patience". You can't get to the end of the game by jumping ahead, you must play each pitch.

As a player, I was always pacing the dugout, encouraging the next guy up to get on base or drive in the run. I would be in the outfield always talking to Tom Jenkins next to me in centerfield and Bob Murphy in rightfield, discussing how we were going to defend the batter, always yelling back into the infield at Phil Honeycutt at shortstop and Les Rogers at third base after they were telling us how many outs and them encouraging us to be ready and how to shift, or yelling back in at Steve Rogers, Cliff Butcher, Jay Weinheimer, Reg Rowe and all our great pitchers to strike out the hitter. That was just me, I played the game with emotions on my sleeve and always thought we would win the game if we still had one out left to play.

In 1970, after getting beat by Arizona State in the 1969 CWS finals, we were playing Arizona State again in the Riverside tournament and down 10-3 in the ninth inning. No hope and no chance of winning. Right?

There are no such things as an 8 run homerun. So, all we could do was take it one pitch at a time. Were we going to win? As long as we had one out left, we were absolutely going to win. But it would take the entire roster to do it. We would have to bat around the order more than once. Words of encouragement, fighting every pitch at the plate, one run at a time. Patience!

Pitch by pitch, run by run, one out left to keep the rally going, then finally, in the most intense inning I have ever played, Steve Caves got a base hit up the middle to win the game. This was a total team effort. The energy and support pulling for each other was off the charts. Believing we could win the game was the key ingredient. But patience won the game.

I know I am being a storyteller again, but I can't help myself. I just want everyone to know the struggles you go through, whatever they may be, you have not only your team behind you. You have an entire TU baseball program of players for several years that know how to win and encourage behind you. You have all our families and friends behind you. You even have people you don't know behind you. I am a very lucky guy to be a part of something so special. You are lucky as well to know each one of us is with you, no matter the situation.

The journey may be long and difficult, but it is a journey so many have traveled and made it to the end. If we have one out left, we will win the game. We just must be "patient," and let the team fight together, taking it one pitch at a time to win the game.

When you are living in the storm of a difficulty in your life, you are probably thinking, I wish this was over. It is too difficult, and I am tired of the pain in my heart and mind. However, there are no shortcuts to making the difficulties and pain go away. You must live the journey. Each step of it.

I was now quickly moving down my path and it was getting darker each step of the way. I was entering into the unknown. Sure, I had great sessions with my doctors and nurses going over what to expect while going through chemotherapy treatments. But until you have experienced it, you don't know how your body and mind will react to the poison dripping into your body.

The chemo treatments were not painful, nor were the side effects afterwards. However, you lose your energy and your appetite. Over a period, I lost my tastebuds. The food just didn't taste good and was bland.

The week after my first chemo treatment was the only time my stomach felt so bad that I threw up. That first week was rough. I guess my body was reacting to this foreign substance now passing through my body. It had to get used to it. I spent most of the days during chemo treatments laying on the sofa. You just feel yucky.

The second week you begin to start feeling better and more normal. However, you begin to start looking ahead to the next week when you must get another treatment, and the cycle begins again.

I was beginning to learn things about myself. I had to accept the fact that I was sick, and there was no other way to be healed. I had to go through the chemo treatments, the side effects, and the upcoming Whipple surgery. I had to live in the moment. But, most importantly, I realized this journey was going to be a long journey. It was going to have dark paths with no light at the end of the journey. The odds of survival were not getting any better. I was living the path that cancer patients must walk. There were no shortcuts.

There were other things I learned about myself. I was still at peace because I had friends, family and so many people praying and supporting me. I felt part of a team. I could not let the team down. I had to keep pushing forward. I had to learn one very important word and apply it to myself each day. That word was "patience".

As I sat in the chemo chair for 6-8 hours twice a week, I brought my iPad and a couple of books. I would also watch a movie on my iPad. There was no leaving the facility until each bag of my "cocktail" was empty. Friends frequently came to visit and spend time with me. My family would bring me lunch. The time seemed to pass quickly.

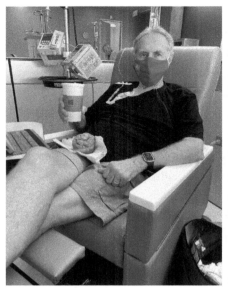

Because of the possibility of Covid we had to wear a mask. I am enjoying breakfast while being given my "chemo cocktail."

The facility consisted of two rooms of over 100 cubicles. One cubicle for each patient. It was bright from the full-length windows and bright lighting. The nurses that treated you each time were always very kind and uplifting. In my several trips and all-day stays, I never saw a nurse have a bad day. They were amazing. The only depressing thing I saw was the number of people coming every day to fill those cubicles. Often patients would come in the morning, leave after their treatments were completed and then an afternoon shift of patients would come for their treatments. The number of people facing cancer was staggering.

You might say, each of us cancer patients were facing insurmountable odds of recovery. I was in this game and expecting to win, but I knew it was going to be a long game. I could not make it go any faster. I could not jump ahead to the surgery, and remove the cancer. I had no control over curing my cancer.

What I had on my side, was "hope for a cancer free life". I had a team of doctors and nurses doing everything they could to make sure I was given treatments to kill the cancer. I had friends and family by my side giving me support every day. I had God holding my right hand. I now had the desire to document my journey, which was giving me positive energy and much needed mental therapy.

Most importantly, I had come to the realization that this was going to be a long journey. There would be difficult moments along the way, and I learned there are no shortcuts. It takes "patience" to let the team working together and to take one pitch at a time. If we had one out left, we could win the game.

10 |

Journal Entry August 7, 2022 - Butterflies

One more lesson I learned the hard way. I mention it because a few of you have expressed the same thing.

I have never been good at calling friends that are sick or had situations occur in their life that needed a friend to give them a call or give them a visit. Why, because "I didn't know what to say". So, I didn't reach out. I stayed in my little comfort zone. I was totally wrong and will never forgive myself in a couple instances that I won't get into, because of my insecurities.

But I learned my lesson from many of you. It isn't about "what you say", it is about "that you did say something". You did reach out. Now, don't get me wrong, I am not asking for more calls, etc. Everyone has been amazing! But, not necessarily for me, but in any other circumstances you may encounter, when a friend needs to hear from you, then "do it". If they have cancer, it is ok to use the Big "C" word and talk about it. But it doesn't have to be about that either, but don't avoid the subject.

Now, another story to illustrate my point. "I know, here he goes again". I will pick on Tom Jenkins this time. Tom, like many of you, is great at calling and just checking in. It was just a short call, but it meant a lot. I know Tom will disagree, but he is not some great orator that has all the right words to say. He just calls and we visit about anything.

Tom called the other day and this time we had a long call. My wife asked who that was, because passing by she heard a little bit of what we were talking about. She said, "What were you guys talking about? I replied...."butterflies". I know that is not a manly subject for two dirty old ballplayers to be talking about. Maybe it was the appropriate subject since we both played in the "grassy outfield" together. No turf out there. You see, we have bugs crawling around in the grass and maybe an occasional butterfly or bee. When you looked in the outfield you would see me, Tom Jenkins or Bob Murphy holding up our fingers. You thought we were signaling how many outs. We were holding up our fingers to see if that butterfly flying around would land on our finger. But we had the infielders convinced we were ready for the next pitch and how many outs there were. This is just a little secret among us outfielders. Don't you remember your little league games and you look in the outfield and you might find them sitting on the grass playing in the dirt? Well, that's where playing in the outfield grass and all kinds of nature around you is where it all begins. So, don't be too harsh on those kids sitting down in the outfield during the pitch, they are learning the fine art of being a great outfielder.

So, my point of all this, just call and talk about butterflies or something. That's all that matters.

To save mine and Tom's manly reputation....Tom and Marsha are trying to save the monarch butterflies by planting "milk weed", a favorite for butterflies. So, that is why we were talking butterflies when my wife passed by. It's amazing they migrate to South America and back every year! Anyway, we are clear on that now. It's ok for "real men" to talk about butterflies. (I think it could be an old age thing too)

I hope everyone has a beautiful day! Oh, and by the way, learn from my mistakes and don't be afraid to call that friend that needs to hear from you.

Talk about butterflies or whatever is of interest to you

In my journal entry on August 7, 2022, I shared a story about "butterflies". You are probably thinking the chemo treatments are starting to affect my mind. Well, you could be right. I find, and you will notice later in my journal entries, I sometimes get creative in my stories. Sometimes, possibly, too creative. Anyway, it was one of those creative moments that I wandered into talking about butterflies.

Sometimes in our lives, we encounter a moment when a friend needs a phone call. But we don't make the phone call because we don't know what to say. I found myself doing this twice with very close friends. Although it was several years ago, I let those opportunities pass by without my calling them. It bothered me for several years, and I never forgave myself for being fearful of finding the right words to say.

I learned the hard way. When I was sick with prostate cancer in 2008 and again now in 2022, I had friends call just to check in with me. My friend, Tom, was great at calling to see how I was doing. Tom did not have any special training on the proper words to say when he called. He was calling as a friend. His calls were heartfelt and very much appreciated. Sometimes the calls were short and other times we would have longer calls. So, from the receiving end of getting the call, it wasn't important what Tom had to say, but that he did call. I always looked forward to getting those calls from Tom. They really lifted my spirits.

If you have a friend that needs a call, don't worry about what you are going to say, it will come to you. Don't be afraid to ask them how they are doing or talk about the difficulty they are going through. Sometimes they just need someone to listen. Being able to talk to a friend about the pain they have in their hearts or experiencing in their bodies can be a therapeutic moment for them. Also, talking to a friend about something totally different can also help them take their mind off their difficulty for a few minutes. Whatever the need, they will be appreciative if you took the time to check in with them.

Journal Entry August 10, 2022 – Unnamed Friends

Good morning, everyone. I have taken my nausea meds this morning and hoping they work. But before I retire to the couch, I wanted to share something with you. First, I have elected to be more public with my journey because my family wants me to be transparent with them and several of you continue to ask how I am doing as you send me your prayers and support. The blessings and support are priceless. I am very blessed!

It seems each day I learn another lesson as I meet each unpredictable feeling and some that are emotional. I look forward to what I am going to learn each day.

I am aware of a few of our baseball teammates and families that are going through similar chemo treatments and serious illness that I have been trusted to keep private at this time. I can pray for them and talk to them by name. I am honored to have this trust. So, please give your prayers and support to our "unnamed friends" as you gave it to me. They will feel the same as I do.

To each of you that have or will someday, in some capacity, face trials, just keep the faith and know you have so much support. To my "unnamed brothers and sisters", I came across this quote this morning that I wanted to share with you. "Look for flowers of Joy growing in the rich soil of adversity." We are going to overcome and beat these tough times.

Someday soon, we will celebrate together. Have a great day everyone!

Flowers of joy growing in the rich soil of adversity

As I continued to travel along my journey, friends often told me my journal entries were helpful and motivating. In several cases, I was told to keep writing and sharing my experiences. I also noticed several people were joining my Facebook page and sharing my journal entries with their followers. As I have mentioned previously, the response I received from others gave me energy to keep pushing forward. But most importantly, it was not only therapeutic to me to write my journals, but the feedback I received was humbling and appreciated.

From my writings and experiences, another group of people began reaching out to me as well. These were those I called my "unnamed friends". These were friends that did not want to make their experiences public but wanted the support and prayers from their friends and those supporting me. I was humbled and honored to receive their trust that I could be that friend they could reach out to and share their experiences with someone that was facing the same difficulties as they were.

You never know who is keeping a difficulty private but needs someone to talk to. As you face your difficult periods in life, you also never know who is watching how you handle it that could be helpful to them someday. I have always felt the obstacles in our lives are also opportunities to learn and grow. As I mentioned in my journal entry, "Look for flowers of joy growing in the rich soil of adversity."

SOMETIMES WE NEED SOMEONE TO SIMPLY BE THERE... NOT TO FIX ANYTHING OR DO ANYTHING IN PARTICULAR, BUT TO LET US FEEL WE ARE SUPPORTED AND CARED ABOUT.

12

Journal Entry August 15, 2022 - Winning Isn't Easy

Good morning, everyone. It is a Monday morning, which is supposed to be my good week. But it seems my bad week after my second chemo treatment lasted longer. Maybe it is the accumulative effect of chemo. Those of you that have been down this path know what I am talking about. For me, I am still learning.

One thing I learned this week, which we all know, is "winning isn't easy." If it was, we would never fail. When I hear from Larry Byrd and Steve Bowling this week and the stuff they are going through to recover from their surgeries and the difficulties our "unnamed foxhole friends" are going through chemo and other difficulties, there is always one common theme. "Winning isn't easy". It is hard work, and there are no shortcuts.

When I started on this journey of beating this cancer, I never once had thoughts of "self-pity" or "why me"? They were not allowed. However, don't get the distorted notion that I think I am above all others, and I have control. That is farthest from the truth. I have my bad physical and emotional moments, but I am like you, I am a fighter, and I am blessed with the hundreds giving me prayers and support each day. I had more amazing phone calls, texts, and visits this week of encouragement. The energy I get from those is just like a "shot of inspiration" to keep my eye on the goal. We all remember the hard work we had to put in to get ready for the game and the adversities we encountered to eventually come out the winner. This is no different.

The doctors and nurses told me I would be a better patient if I would get out and exercise, play golf, go fishing or whatever I could handle to be in the best shape possible when it is time for surgery. So, I hope to be better at getting out and push through the "yuckiness feelings".

Keith and Jim landing a big brown trout

This week I was supposed to be on a fly-fishing trip with Keith Yarger and Jim Beasley around Steamboat Springs, Colorado. But I had to cancel. That was tough, but they promised to send pictures. Most of you know how much I enjoy fly fishing. There is an old saying, which I shared with my pastor a few months ago. "Would you rather me be in church dreaming of fly fishing, or be on the river fly fishing and being closer to God"? I choose the latter. So, I will miss my "God moments" this week. I don't think my pastor agreed with my assessment.

I am at the stage of the "transparent path of my journey" of continuing to take it step by step. It does seem like this path is always uphill. There are no forks in the road, "turn here the journey is shorter" or "turn here the path is downhill." There is only one path.

Being closer to God while fly fishing on the river

As I take this journey, I don't know what else to say, but to keep thanking you for your prayers of support. Not only for me, but for the others as well. It makes a huge difference! So, this week, as I realize again, "winning isn't easy", I came upon these words of encouragement. "When you bump into massive difficulties on your life-path, I want you to consider it "pure Joy". As you bounce off these "impossibilities," My everlasting arms are wide open - ready to catch you, calm you, and help you do what does not seem possible."

Have a great week!

One thing I want to make very clear when you are facing cancer or a difficult time in your life, "you are not being punished by God." Sometimes the world wants to find blame and try to convince us we are being punished by God. The world we live in is full of tragedy, sickness, and difficult times. God does not wish us to go through bad times, but because we live in a sinful world, we will encounter tough times in our lives. However, it is during these times we often call upon God to help us. So, don't let the world convince you your period of trials is your fault. By the same token, keep your head up and look to God to give you the strength to stay strong. Self-pity will lead to depression and hopelessness. Looking to God for help, will give you hope, and the will to continue. As I have said earlier, "Let Hope In".

My journey was beginning to get more difficult each day. The chemo treatments were starting to take a toll on my body and mind. I had periods of more pain than others. I found myself lying on the sofa or in the bed for several hours each day. I never felt good or like myself. I always felt yucky. I also began to lose my appetite and taste buds. So, when I did eat, I could not taste it. This led to significant weight loss. I eventually lost over 40 pounds.

As we continue down the paths of our difficulties, it can be tiring and wearing on our minds and bodies. We cannot see the end. All we see is more difficulty ahead. When the body is hurting the mind starts wondering if we can make it. We start looking for a shortcut and a quick fix to make our difficult path easier. But we quickly discover, there is no quick fix. We start to realize this journey is not going to be easy. So, it is decision time. Do I have the will to finish whatever adversities are looming ahead? Or, am I going to quit and not finish the journey? Remember, as long as we have one out left in the game, we can still win.

"When you bump into massive difficulties on your life-path, I want you to consider it "pure Joy". As you bounce off these "impossibilities," My everlasting arms are wide open - ready to catch you, calm you, and help you do what does not seem possible."

13

Journal Entry August 17, 2022 – Being Inspired and Blessed

Warning....this may take me awhile, but something I must share. So, pick your favorite beverage and read on or stop now. Before I go on, please say a little prayer for Larry Byrd and our "unnamed friends" tonight.

Let me jump to the end of the day first. Then, I will go back to the top of the day and share the rest of what started out as a crappy day. However, it was supposed to be a good day. But, it ended on a beautiful note.

What has started as a dreadful journey with nothing but the unknown around each corner has turned into an amazing journey that I am so thankful to be traveling. I would not change this journey for anything. I know that sounds crazy for someone that has pancreatic cancer. But it is what it is, so make the most of it.

I know Suzi Byrd won't mind me sharing a few tidbits from our conversation. First, and most importantly, Larry is back in the hospital with severe stomach pain, and they can't seem to determine the cause. He has had and is going to have more painful and difficult days ahead until they get to the bottom of it. Prayers for you my brother, Larry!!

Larry and I were going to have lunch this week with Mark Calvert, Wayne McCombs, and a couple others. I texted Larry to find the best day but never got a response. So, I decided to give him a call. Suzi answered and said, "I just picked up the phone to give you a call." First, I find the news about Larry and his awful pain. Then in typical Larry and Suzie mode, she flips the discussion about me and how I am doing. We talk and talk and each word she utters just fills me and gives me strength. She has been through several chemo sessions and has lived this journey I am on for several years. As she shares her experiences, they are so much like mine. I asked her if I should continue to share my journey outwardly, like I am doing now, and without hesitation, she said, yes, you must do it. It helps you and so many others out there that have no clue what we have been going through. It helps people we don't even know. The more she speaks, the more the tears well up in my eyes. I know, there is "no crying in baseball" and dirty old ball players don't cry. Well, I did three times today, two on the outside and one on the inside.

I know I say this a lot, but what Larry and Suzi have endured and the inspiration I get from them, well there just aren't words that say it adequately. I am sorry Suzi, but I just have to say the journey you have traveled has helped me so much. And all our friends out there. Love you both!

Back to the top of the morning. Like I said, this was supposed to be a good day and a lunch with friends. But, I woke up with very low blood pressure. I just moved from the bed to the sofa. My wife got me up walking and drinking more fluids. I protested, but she would not give up. "You must do this!" Never go against your wife, they always know best. So, I sat up enough to get a few ounces of water down and my blood pressure started going down. Shortly, Ken Knight calls and says he is going to a doctor's appointment and wanted to know if it was ok to drop by. Of course, it is! We are talking and having a much-needed visit, then I start telling him about the support, prayers and emails I receive. I couldn't help myself, and here come the tears again. I shared with him some of the comments and emails I continually receive. It makes this journey so amazing. Something I would not have experienced without having to walk it. As Suzi told me, we would not change this journey for anything. The love is so huge. The reward at the end of the journey is worth every difficult step.

I know I shouldn't single anyone out, but I go against the grain anyway, because I just wanted to single out a few people that gave me emails that just went straight to my heart. But, all of you do this to me. First, Terrell Lester, Bruce Riddle, Steve Heldebrand, Debbie Almohandis, Steve Bowling, Steve Rogers, Bill Minnerick, Alicia Connor Todd and Jackson Todd, Roger Adams, Tom Jenkins, and Greg and Kelly Jefferies, and on and on. Thank you

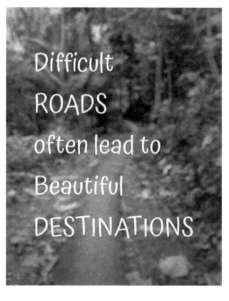

for what you have said and gone beyond. Sorry Terrell, but those of you that remember, Terrell was a Tulsa World sportswriter covering TU baseball all those years. I have read and reread your email so many times. I know, sorry, the tears start flowing again. That's the third time today.

As I am visiting Ken Knight, Wes Shaw is traveling from Texas and wanted to visit me and Brian. I say, that would be awesome. Pick me up and let's go. As we enter the room, Brian is asleep. I wake him up and he sees us both with wide open eyes. Brian and Wes played together at TU and hadn't seen each other for 15 years.

The joy in the room was huge! Here came the tears, but I was able to keep them inward this time. While we were visiting with Brian, Jackson

Todd calls, and we had a facetime chat. All four of us. It was so much fun and another reward for the day.

As we got back in Wes's truck, he said, "well that was inspirational". Yes, Wes, see what I mean when you visit Brian. He just has this magic that he pours over us. Wow, you too!

He takes me back home, and back to the couch for some rest. Then the phone rang, I didn't recognize the number, but something told me to answer it. I did, and it was one of my best friends, Dick Brown, who many of you played with and against in little leagues and high school. We played together at NEO JC, and he signed with OU. He had been trying to reach some of the old 1969 baseball guys. He started searching on Facebook. He typed in 1969 and meant to type in OU but typed TU instead. He accidentally found our FB page. After several calls, he found someone (I think Steve Irvine) that had my phone number and gave me a call. After several minutes of reliving the past, he started asking about Tom Jenkins, Roger Adams, Steve Caves, Steve Irvine, Stan Irvine and Steve Chrisman. We had not talked in over 20 years. Another lift for the day. Dick, if you are on our FB page and a member, all your buddies are here. Welcome to the "dirty old ballplayers" and families and friends water hole. We love to stay in contact with each other. This is where you find true "foxhole friends".

For those of you that made it to the end of this lengthy post, all I can say is, thank you for making this journey a blessing. I will never regret this journey! Like Suzi Byrd and I discussed, when it comes down to it, we are in a "Win, Win" situation! We either make it through the journey and continue to live a beautiful life with our friends and family or we reunite in Heaven someday and celebrate then. This is a winning deal. We are going to beat it.

Sometimes you must live through difficult times to find amazing goodness. That is exactly what I was beginning to discover as I was walking the path of my journey. Did I want pancreatic cancer and then to live through all those chemo treatments? Absolutely not! But when I shared with others my story and saw how they had rallied behind me, it was a feeling I never would have experienced.

When you are walking down a path of very difficult times in your life, think about what you are doing. You are just trying to keep your head up and keep pushing forward. We often hear the words, "the greater the risk, the greater the rewards." I think it can also be said "the greater the obstacle in your path, the greater the reward." I am learning more about myself each day as I wake up in the mornings and discover there is another and different obstacle in my path. As I get through one obstacle and then another, I grow more convinced that I can survive those bad days. I can win that pitch or that inning. It begins to build confidence in your spirit and prepares you for the next bad thing around the corner. You are creating wins. Wins that you can call upon when you encounter a similar situation. Ah! I have been here before, and here is what I learned how to deal with it. On the flip side of this coin, think how that experience might help someone else.

When I called Larry and Suzi, I knew they had already encountered a situation like what I was about to experience. When you are facing something new, don't try to fight your way through it if you can open a book and learn how to handle it. However, there are no manuals that lay it out step by step on how to beat cancer. There are no manuals with the magic formula on how to handle the loss of your mother, a child, or a close friend. There are no manuals on how to take away the pain of divorce. Yes, there are lots of self-help books. But has the author lived the situation?

I could read all types of information on the internet about cancer and the chemo treatments and surgeries to follow. But how powerful it is to talk to a person that experienced it first-hand. Find a friend or someone who has experienced it and can talk to you about the bad days and what it was like having the pain going through your soul, mind, and body. Find someone to talk about all those questions you want to ask. What did you do? What was it like? How did you feel?

Because I had friends I could trust with my innermost thoughts and could relate to my situation, it meant the world to me. I had those friends with Larry and Suzi. They had experienced it, and they were glad to share with me anything I wanted to talk about. They were not trained in what to say. They were just like me. I have found it can be detrimental to you in getting past those difficult periods if you just keep it private and not share it. Find the Larry and Suzi in your life, and let them in on your pain and helpless feelings.

We can't **HELP** EVERYONE, but **EVERYONE** CAN HELP **SOMEONE**

You know what? Now that you have lived that tough patch in your life, use it to help someone else. Now that I am living the life of someone who has had cancer, had numerous chemotherapy treatments, and the Whipple surgery, I have come out on the other side of the journey with the passion to give what I can to someone that has a need. I want to be a "Larry and Suzi" to someone else. It is not about "me", it is about my experience. It is about "you".

14

Journal Entry August 26, 2022 – Weaker Everyday

As for my latest, I just finished my third chemo treatment and have one more to go in two weeks. After that I will do a CT scan to see how things look. My prayer would be no more chemo and go to the Whipple surgery. But we shall see. It is what it is!

It seems after each chemo treatment I experience something different, other than the constants of no appetite and yucky feelings. I now have sensitivity to cold and must wear gloves to get anything out of the refrigerator, especially the freezer. They tweak my "cocktail" each time to make the side effects less severe. This time I have hiccups all the time and trembling hands. Little difficult typing this update! I did try to play golf with Ken Knight, Tom Jenkins, and Roger Adams last week, but that was a disaster. I could barely hold and swing the club, let alone hit the ball. So, after one hole, I had my wife come get me and take me back to the couch. I walked around the block the other night. Need to do this more often. I don't go out in big crowds while on chemo because if I got Covid it would stop everything. But I have lunch with friends occasionally. That is nice. So, the journey continues, step by step, day by day. Thank you for all the prayers and support.

I have traveled further and further down my path. But it is getting more difficult. I have finished my third chemo treatment and can tell after each treatment that I am getting weaker each day. I have so many medications I cannot keep them straight. Some of the side effects are the same and predictable, but I am finding new side effects as well. Some are more difficult than others. For me, I found my most difficult side effect and most depressing was the hiccups. I had them constantly. They would never go away. I could not sleep because of the hiccups. I could not eat because of the hiccups. I was getting depressed because of the hiccups. I was one "big hiccup." On top of the hiccups, my expected sensitivity to cold and heat was getting worse. I had expected this and was better prepared mentally.

The kids had pitched in their money and bought me several items that would help me as I was taking chemotherapy treatments. Along with short and long sleeve sweatshirts that had zippers in just the right place to access my port, they bought me gloves and thick socks. My care package had several snacks I could eat while sitting in the chemo treatment chair, books to read and numerous odd and ends of interesting things to keep me busy.

But, with all those nice things in my care package, there was nothing for the hiccups. You can tell, those days of the hiccups are forever implanted in my brain. I was usually laying on the sofa because of no energy and not feeling well, but I thought I would take the doctors' orders and try getting outside. I agreed to give it a try playing golf with my golfing buddies. However, it did not go well for me. I was so weak by now I could barely hold the golf club let alone swing it. Also, I was struggling to sit upright in the golf cart. So, rather than ruin a beautiful day of golf with the guys, I called my wife to come get me after only one hole. I guess, to my credit, I did give it a try. But it was back home to the sofa.

I knew the chemo treatments were necessary for my chance of beating cancer, but as I was starting to experience the side effects, the more I was wanting them to be over. Partly because they made me ill and not feel well, but mostly I was starting to get anxious to get the Whipple surgery. I knew this was a very complex and difficult surgery that had its own high risk, but this was the only way I was going to beat cancer. I wanted to get to the "fix it" stage. As the days and weeks crept by, it seemed like it was going to take forever to get to the December schedule of the surgery.

With Covid still around, I could not afford to get the disease. It would stop my treatments and put everything on hold. So, I stayed indoors most of the time. Although my attempt to do something outside, like play golf or go fishing was not going to work, I was only able to take short walks in the neighborhood. It felt good to be outside, but I did not have the energy to go very far. It seemed I was losing the fight. The will to push forward was still there, but the body was not able to keep up with my desires. I did not feel like reading so I just laid on the sofa and watched endless hours of TV. I felt like I was living "ground hog day" every day. But I had no choice. One step at a time, and be patient. This was going to be a long journey.

Every day seemed like the same. It felt like it was ground hog day over and over

15

Journal Entry August 30, 2022 – Determined to Push Forward

First, let me again thank you for all the prayers and support you have given me and our "unnamed friends". We could not do this without you! Each of you have such huge hearts to spend a few moments thinking about us. Your prayers continue to give us strength to get through the next few hours and days that lie ahead in this journey. Yes, sometimes the effect of chemo makes us just want to get through the next few hours. But, the journey, step by step, keeps moving forward. Still uphill, but I believe I can see a fork in the road up ahead. Just like our "unnamed friends", we are tired and getting weaker with each step, but we have the resolve to beat this terrible disease. It is just unbelievable the number of people that go in and out of the doors of this place. So many people are suffering from cancer. It is heartbreaking.

I just found out about the wife of a close friend that was just diagnosed with cancer. Fortunately, like Larry and Suzi do for me, I was able to talk to her and help her with what to expect going forward. This is why the journey I am traveling on is so good for me. I can help someone else. I know that sounds crazy, and I hope it does not come across the wrong way, but we all have faced difficulties in our lives. We come out on the other side stronger, more determined, and better people. You know, in your own little world you have faced things that you did not like while going through it, but when it was over, you looked back and learned about yourself, that you have a life experience to draw strength from and that in some small way you can use that experience to be a better person and help someone else. If nothing but just a little nod of the head or comment of encouragement because you can relate to what they are going through. Life's little lessons.

I have finished my third chemo treatment and have one more next Tuesday. I pray it is my last one. I am ready to go into the "fix it stage" and have the surgery. The side effects of this round have been worse than the previous rounds. It seems the side effects have a different surprise in addition to the normal side effects. This time, I have had constant non-stop hiccups. Some hiccups seem to get caught in my throat where I can't breathe and start gasping for air. Who would ever think you could choke on a hiccup. Well, you can! A new experience. On September 14, I go for a CT scan to see the results of the chemo treatments. This is that fork in the road I see a little farther up the path. On the 19th, I will meet with the doctor and determine the next steps. So, I am getting there slowly but surely. One step at a time.

I am so ready for football to start this week. I keep telling myself I am going to TU's first home game. Probably thinking too big, but I would love to sit there in the stands with cool breezes watching TU again. We shall see.

Often when we are facing difficult moments, we get physically and emotionally tired. We just want the problem to go away. We can't see the end of the road. We only see another curve in the road that has another unknown surprise around the corner. What is it going to be this time? But all we can do is keep taking one step after another. Preparing ourselves to fight through the next difficult moment. This is when we must reach deep within our soul and keep moving forward. When I had the hiccups during my chemo treatments, it was one of those low moments when I wasn't sure I could keep going. I had the hiccups 24 hours each day. Getting any sleep was impossible. Several times I would have a deep hiccup that caused me to lose my breath. As hard as I tried, I couldn't get my breath back. I had no more air in my lungs and couldn't get the hiccup to release so I could take another breath. Just when I thought I was going to pass out, the hiccup released. I finally got medicine to take care of these hiccups and was starting to get relief. These were very difficult moments to experience.

I knew somewhere ahead of me on my journey I would reach the fork in the road when the chemo treatments would be over, and I would enter another phase of the journey. I called it my "fix it" stage. This is the stage where I would be going through the very complex and high-risk Whipple surgery. But, I knew there were no short-

The fork in the road that has the unknown surprise around the next corner

cuts on this path. I would have to face those dark days soon.

When you face those difficulties in your life, the path will have smooth phases and phases when it is very difficult. Keep your eye on the big picture, and know this day will pass. This is easier said than done. However, it is a path you must live and keep the faith. Let hope in and keep your faith because you can live through this. Know that this difficult patch in your life will have an end, and better days are ahead.

16

Journal Entry September 9, 2022 – Foxhole Friends

Now that I have finished my fourth round of chemo, I will be getting a CT scan on the 14th. The CT scan will determine the effectiveness of the chemo, and what path we take next. I know, another path that I have no idea where it is going and what is at the end of the path. This morning I am finding myself reflecting on this journey while I am in sort of a temporary pause for a few days.

When I decided to document my journey, I had no idea what that looked like. What should I say? What does being transparent really mean? Should I share the bad along with the good? How will it be received? Will it come across as self-pity and self-serving? That is the last thing I wanted. Where will this journey take me? What if the ending is not a happy ending. So many thoughts go through my head.

The journey has been uphill, but still full of encouragement from my "foxhole friends"

I have always loved the mountains, the beautiful streams, the open meadows full of flowers, the mountain lake untouched by any fisherman, and the sighting of an occasional moose or, if lucky a bear. The clean cool breezes flowing through the Aspen trees. In my "mind's eye", this is the type of path I have been walking. Up to this point, all up hill.

So, on my journey I reached the midpoint of the mountain. There are paths going in different directions, still up hill. Hmm, which one will be my next path? But there is this big boulder right here in front of me under a nice shady tree. So, here I am taking a pause from whatever is next and just going to look over my shoulder and reflect on what I just experienced and what I learned.

My rock that provided me a place to rest and reflect on the path I have traveled

First and foremost, I do not wish cancer on anyone and the treatments you must go through to cure it. It is not fun, and you just hope tomorrow you will feel better. But, you quickly realize so many people have gone through this before you, and you just must suck it up and get moving.

Looking at what I have experienced to this point has been one of the most rewarding, life-changing experiences in my life. I am a much better person because of this journey. How can I say that? It's easy. When you are given so much love, prayers, and support from those you cherish the most and then you receive it from people you don't even know, that are helped by your journey, it is just overwhelming. You have no idea what you are doing for me, and others like me. Your true self is shining through.

As you know, I am a fighter. It seems like I have always had to fight extra hard for what I wanted, so it comes naturally to me, and I thrive on it. But you are too. That is why I wanted to play baseball for TU. I grew up with these guys and they are winners and are for each other over self.

Larry Byrd, Les Rogers and me

Growing up, I was a year older than Larry Byrd and Les Rogers. They were great athletes and better people. I looked up to them and yes, envious of their God given ability. But I was not even close to them in ability. So, to meet their standards I had to work harder and harder every day. Then, I go to TU and get on a team of my peers that drove me to be better and taught me that a true team is made of winners. Then, I wrote a book about the history of TU baseball and learned about the guys that followed our teams. They were true champions and amazing people. I am very blessed to have this experience. To be one of the "TU dirty old ballplayers".

Then to top it off, I am honored to be on the TU Letterwinners Board. Now I can give back to the university and the athletes that were just like us when were in school. To be associated with these amazing men and women helping others, is just the icing on the cake. I am truly blessed to be part of these former athletes.

So, as I am sitting here on my big boulder staring at these other paths before me, what have I learned? These thoughts I have shared previously, but they sort of stick out to me. I guess I needed to read them again to keep me going.

Sometimes life just doesn't seem fair. Life isn't fair, so be prepared to deal with those times when you think you are not being treated as you think you should. Life throws us curve balls. You must learn to hit the curve ball.

I told my brother that I am so lucky to have so many friends that I play golf with, go fishing, and just stay in touch with on Facebook and email. Then, he told me something that really struck me. He said, "Roger, those aren't just friends that are here today, or that call you, or you visit with on Facebook, or you played ball with all those years. What you have are "fox-hole friends". Think about that statement. He was right on! My friends aren't just friends, they are more than that! Think about what this label means to each of us. We are "foxhole friends"! Wow! Now that is special. That is why I keep saying each of you are amazing! Each of you is special.

As I travel my journey, I found a word that has become a key reminder as I am walking the path. The new word I am learning to apply to myself is "patience".

In 1970, after getting beat by Arizona State in the 1969 CWS finals, we were playing Arizona State again in the Riverside tournament and down 10-3 in the ninth inning. No hope and no chance of winning. Right?

There are no such things as an 8 run homerun. So, all we could do was take it one pitch at a time. Were we going to win? If we had one out left, we were absolutely going to win. But, it would take the entire roster to do it. We would have to bat around the order more than once. Words of encouragement, fighting every pitch at the plate, one run at a time. Patience!

Pitch by pitch, run by run, one out left to keep the rally going, then finally, in the most intense inning I have ever played, Steve Caves got a base hit up the middle to win the game.

This was a total team effort. The energy and support pulling for each other was off the charts. Believing we could win the game was the key ingredient. But, patience won the game.

The struggles you go through, whatever they may be, you not only have your team behind you. You have an entire TU baseball program of players that know how to win and to encourage behind you. You have all our families and friends behind you. You even have people you don't know behind you.

"Look for flowers of Joy growing in the rich soil of adversity."

"Winning isn't easy". "When you bump into massive difficulties on your life-path, I want you to consider it "pure Joy". As you bounce off these "impossibilities", My everlasting arms are wide open - ready to catch you, calm you, and help you do what does not seem possible."

So, as I sit here reflecting on these words again, I am reminded of whatever path I am supposed to take next, I have the best people in my life praying and supporting me. My true "foxhole friends". Thank you, I love you, and I am a very blessed person to be on this journey!

I was at a point in my journey where I knew there was going to be a change in direction. A big change. Going through chemotherapy treatments were not the final solution. There were no expectations the cancer would be gone. But, the hope was it would shrink in size to give the surgeon more room to operate near the aorta. I had read enough about the Whipple surgery to know it was one of the two most difficult and complex surgeries. It was a high-risk surgery that still had high risk after a successful surgery. But, it was my only hope.

I had reached a point in my journey that provided time to reflect on what I had experienced. I was tired, losing weight, had low energy levels, and still feeling yucky. I knew the easy part was behind me and the most difficult days were ahead. Although my path had some difficult moments, overall, it was rather predictable and smooth. In comparison to what I was going to experience, it felt like I was walking uphill in the mountains with meadows of beautiful flowers. However, that was going to change in a big way. The path ahead was dark and full of ragged rocks. It was not smooth and wide.

When you are going through a difficult period in your life, remember this is a long journey. Think about the obstacles you have faced already and pushed through them. Remember the lessons you learned. Know that you are a stronger person having experienced those bad days. As I have said many times, take it one step at a time. Be patient and face each day with the courage of believing you can do this. Reach out to those that are supporting you, and share with them your thoughts so they can help you. Trust your "foxhole friends" and know they are traveling this journey with you. God has your right hand, and your friends have your left hand. You are not alone.

The path ahead was going to be difficult

17

Journal Entry September 19, 2022 - When You Fall, Don't Give Up

If You Fall, Don't Give Up

Looking at the picture of the tree, well, it says it all. "When you fall, don't give up!"

Just like so many of us and your family and friends, we have tough times in life. Having cancer is in the top 5. But when you have so many people loving, caring, and praying for you, then hold on to that support and keep fighting on. Your prayers are working and being answered. We haven't crossed the finish line yet; I can't see it yet. I met with the doctor today to go over my CT scan. He was very pleased to tell me the chemo treatments are working, and the tumor has shrunk from 1.1 cm to .8 cm. He has me on a plan of 4 more chemo treatments starting tomorrow, Whipple surgery in November or December and another 4 more chemo treatments after surgery. The road is still long but I can see a plan taking shape.

Thank you for praying during the first step. But, I still need you walking with me on this long journey. I love you all!

I love the picture of the tree that had fallen over, yet it was still giving life to new branches. It didn't die and turn into rotting wood. The tree said I may not be standing tall as I used to, but I can still fight and continue to be productive and not give up. I can be an inspiration to someone thinking this is the end, I am done! Well, I am not done! I can give life to new growth.

I had received good news from my fourth CT scan. It showed the treatments were working so that I could continue down my path as we had planned. The cancer was shrinking and giving the surgeon more room to operate near the aorta. However, this was just a milestone in the journey. The path was going to be difficult, but I was still moving forward. I was hoping the chemo treatments would be over, but my oncologist wanted to give me the best odds of a successful surgery by ordering another four treatments. Not exactly good news but I did not have a choice. Remember? Be patient. Stay strong. If you fall or don't get the news you wanted to hear, don't give up.

As I have said, your journey of difficulty may be long. It will have twists and turns you don't expect. You may think you are not making any progress and cannot see the end. When will it end? When will it get better? These are normal reactions to living through a difficult period of your life. Don't beat yourself up. Hang in there. Pick yourself up and apply those lessons you are learning. Keep moving forward and remember, be "patient".

18

Journal Entry September 20, 2022 – The Raw Moments

Before I share with you the next phase of my journey, please remember our "unnamed" foxhole friends that are struggling and need your prayers. Don't forget them just because they don't have a name!

Before I got the results of my CT scan, I shared with you that I had reached a crest on the mountain that had several different paths ahead and a big boulder under the shade of a beautiful Aspen tree. I had climbed on the boulder and not knowing what path to take, I took a rest in the journey to look where I had come from and reflect on the many experiences I had traveled. It was a good rest and a much-needed moment to reflect on and learn from the past. Something I am very much going to need going forward. The most rewarding and the energy I get moving forward is the number of people praying and supporting me. The numbers literally grow every day. I cannot thank you enough. It gives me strength. You are amazing!

As I have stated several times, this is my specific journey, but it is also a journey to inform those of you that always ask how I am doing and how they can help me. But I have found that maybe my journey will help someone that is going through a tough time or will have to deal with cancer someday. If it helps someone, then it is the right thing to do. I pray it is.

So, now that I got my positive results from the CT scan has shrunk the cancer, I have a plan going forward. I was hoping I could move right to surgery, but the plan calls for two more months (4 treatments) of chemo before the very difficult Whipple surgery in November or December, followed by 4 more chemo treatments after surgery.

The path ahead will be difficult with many twists and turns

Well, now that I know which path I am going to travel, it is time for me to jump off my big boulder and get ready for the next phase of the journey. As I stare up ahead of the path, it has beautiful, flowered meadows on the left and a beautiful mountain stream on the right side running down the mountain among lots of tall Pine and Aspen trees. It sounds so peaceful. But the path is still uphill. It looks to be a gradual uphill slope and somewhat familiar to what I have already traveled. But, beyond that the path becomes very narrow, much steeper and darkly shaded. The meadow on the left is gone and replaced with tall trees that are clinging on the sides of a sheer cliff. The stream on the right is now several feet below and barely visible. The path is no longer smooth to walk on and has become very steep. It is not a straight path and has several twists and turns. I cannot see the end of the path let alone where it leads me.

As I have done my best to be as transparent as possible, there were a few moments, I guess I could call them my "raw moments". I have not shared them before but to be fully transparent and hopefully helpful to someone else that may travel a similar journey, then I should share those as well.

When I heard I had cancer, that was bad enough. I knew anyone having cancer was not a good thing, and that you could die from it. But when I heard I had pancreatic cancer, that was a totally different game. I had not known anyone that survived pancreatic cancer. Then, I started reading about pancreatic cancer and there was this Whipple surgery that could cure the cancer in some instances, but the survival rate of those getting Whipple surgery was 3-5 years. This sent my mind swirling and thinking all different kinds of thoughts. After reading too much on the internet, (by the way, the internet is a great resource, but it can be a bad thing too), I was feeling conflicted. I walked over to my wife and told her, "Well, I have always wondered if I would like to die suddenly or know when I was going to die. I guess I now know when I am going to die." This was a tough "raw moment" that I could no longer see any further than just a few months ahead. With my eyes getting teary, but not scared, she put her arms around me and said let's talk. We talked about the now, we talked about the future, we talked about the unknown, and we talked about my faith in God. In the perfect caregiving way she has, I soon felt better and more determined to beat this terrible disease.

Later, I went to bed and had a restless night trying to sleep. Not much sleep is going to happen tonight, but I finally fell asleep probably from exhaustion. The next morning, as I often do, I read my morning devotion. The very first line I read, just like they were printed on the page just that night, it said "Hold out your right hand and I will take care of you." I couldn't believe what I was reading, and the tears came again. I immediately felt at peace with my situation. Now, notice, it did not say God would heal me or cure me, but it didn't say he wouldn't either. It simply says, "I will take care of you". That can mean lots of things!

Wonderful things! As I am traveling my journey, wherever it leads me, I know God has my "right hand". This is why I can truly say I am grateful to be given the experience of my journey. It has changed my life, and I am better for it. What if it has a sad ending? I guess I look at it this way, I am in a Win-Win situation. I will either end up in Heaven with my dad, Coach Shell, and several of our friends that have passed before us. Or, I get to spend more time on this earth with my family, friends and just doing things I have put off for some other day to accomplish. My fighting spirit and my determination says it will be the latter, and I am going to be around several more years on this earth. I really believe it!

Now, why did I share this "raw moment"? I don't know. But I guess to show that many of our friends are also going through tough times right now as well. We all have real life mind swirling "raw moments". But, it is ok! Don't resist those moments but embrace them and then, find the resolve to reach deep in your soul and say I am going to push through these "real life" thoughts. They are not going to consume my life let alone control me. I am going to have patience, knowing winning isn't easy, but I am going to win and beat this situation. Then, you will find peace and the strength to fight on each day one at a time, each step one at a time until you reach the finish line.

Again, this is a journey that I know God has my "right hand", and I know all my family and my "foxhole friends" have my "left hand". They are walking with me and giving me strength to carry on. Thank you. So, hold on, we have a path picked out for us to take and a plan to cross the finish line together. I love you all!

One of the concerns of documenting my journey was the sharing of "raw moments" in public view. I was opening myself up to judgement and exposing my fragile moments to anyone that read these journals. I had said from the beginning, I was going to be transparent and honest. However, I found writing the entries and talking about my journey were a therapy session for me. I was also benefiting from my acknowledgement that this was hard, I had no control and had to give myself up to my doctor's and nurse's judgements and their knowing what to do and when.

Give your burdens to the Lord and He will take care of you.

God will give you peace

What I experienced by opening myself up and being transparent was that although others may not be as transparent, they are no different from me. But they can relate, and it might be helpful to them as well. Sometimes it will help us all to take a moment and look at our inner selves and how we handle difficult periods in our lives. God has said to give him our burdens and He will carry them for us. When we give our burdens to God, you will be amazed how light the load will become. He will help us during those moments when we are frustrated and don't know what to do. He will help us by giving us peace of mind. However, often, God will give us someone among us that wants to share in carrying our burdens as well.

I am not saying every person must share their raw moments in public, but I would imagine you have that "foxhole friend" you can trust to share your private thoughts so they can help you. You will also find they have been waiting to help you with whatever you need as well.

Whether it is writing down your good days and bad days or your raw moments, find that method that works for you to face your problems and difficult moments face to face. Maybe, it is talking to a friend. It always helps us to have someone to share our journey.

19

Journal Entry October 4, 2022 – Winning Doesn't Always Mean Finishing First

Hi everyone,

It has been a while since I sent out an update, so here goes.

I am sad to say we have added another one of our foxhole friends to the "unnamed foxhole friends" list. We have another one of us that has been diagnosed with cancer. It appears to be caught early with a great chance of full recovery. But that means we have about 5/6 of us fighting every day. Keep those prayers coming for our friends.

The last time I reported, I was on the uphill path with meadows on the left and a beautiful stream deep in the forest on the right. But that unavoidable treacherous dark path is getting closer. I am getting more tired each day. But every time I feel down and just want to lay on the sofa or in the bed, I remember all those friends that have it worse than I do. So, press on "Whit", you know what it takes to finish. You have lots of prayers and support pulling for you and waiting for you at the finish line. As I said before, "winning isn't easy", but sometimes a very painful sacrifice is required to pass the finish line. And the more pain, the greater the experience and the satisfaction you get when you cross the finish line.

The last round of chemo really knocked me down for almost two weeks. No appetite, and other side effects really got me this time. I didn't experience my good week, so I assume the accumulation of the chemo treatments is just wearing me down. Talking to some of our unnamed friends, they are experiencing the same. This time, misery doesn't love company! I just want everyone to feel better and have more good days than bad. But, step by step, patience, keep looking forward. This time will pass.

On the good news front, I met with the surgeon who will be performing the Whipple surgery last week. It was a great session, and he answered all my questions, some difficult but real. He was very upfront with me. I came away from the meeting ready to go to surgery right now. But I must finish three more rounds of chemo treatments. I have an 11-hour session tomorrow, followed by the standard wearing a chemo bag at home for two more days. The doctor was very pleased with the results of the chemo treatments and said the tumor was moving away from the arteries that were most concerning. He is confident the surgery can cure the cancer, but since it is close to several lymph nodes, he will take biopsies of the lymph nodes during surgery to ensure it hasn't spread. The surgery will most likely be in December. I have a minor stent replacement on October 31. So, I am encouraged.

Now back to my journey since last reported. It hasn't been a good two weeks. I have found myself reflecting on some key moments in my life that helped me become the scrapper, fighter, and with the will to win and cross the finish line, no matter the sacrifice. I am sure you all have these little moments. These have always been in the deep recesses of my mind and come to the front of my mind when I need them. I needed them this week. Yes, I know more stories.

When I was in elementary school, every summer morning my brother and I would quickly eat breakfast, grab our bats, gloves and balls and go to the street or one of our backyards and play baseball all day. On this day, we had a bully in the neighborhood that wanted to play with us. We said OK. But, during the game he started picking on some of the younger kids and would not leave them alone. Me, being the oldest, but not the biggest, decided I was not going to take it any longer and needed to stand up for our younger baseball friends. I challenged the bully and told him to leave them alone, and he couldn't play any longer. This was the first mistake. He wouldn't stop and was ready to fight. He was probably a foot taller than me and at least 30 pounds heavier. Shoving turned into fighting. I am not sure I landed any punches, but he was wearing me out. I think my head was his punching bag. All the kids were standing around cheering for me, but it sure wasn't helping. Finally, he got me pinned on the ground and just kept pounding away at my head. One of the kids couldn't watch this slaughter any longer and ran and got my mom. She came out swinging and hollering for the bully to get up. I have never seen my mom like this before. She saved me. The next day, with my swollen head and eyes barely able to see, I saw the bully. He was wearing a cast! I found out the bully was taking boxing lessons and broke his hand hitting my head so much. I was hurting all over, but I was the hero of all the kids. Did I win? In their eyes I did, but it was a very painful win. That day, I was a fighter.

While in high school, I did not play football but ran cross country to get in shape for basketball. I was short, skinny, and not built for long distance running. I was a sprinter. I was able to figure out most of the strategies of long-distance running. At the end of the season, we had the city championships. I was our best runner, so there was no chance we would finish anywhere near the leader board. But they gave medals to the top 10 finishers. There was no chance that would happen either. However, I am a scrapper. All I wanted was a medal. Finish 10th and I get a medal. The race was held on the campus of Roger's High School.

I am standing at the starting line and all around me are these tall, long legged, built for distance, runners. Most of the top runners already had scholarships to college as long-distance runners. I am thinking, all I must do is stay close to the leader pack, and then sprint to the finish line. However, they already know this too. The race starts and I am taking two steps to their one long stride. Can I keep this up for two miles? As we get deeper in the race, I am starting to lose contact with the leaders. Probably 10-15 in the pack. It is decision time, if I am going to get a medal, I need to catch these guys. It took a half mile for me to finally catch up with the pack. But I burned just about everything I had in me to do it. On the last mile, the pack started separating as each runner was making their move. I still had 15 runners ahead of me and pulling away. Half a mile to the finish line, I had another decision to make. How bad do I want that medal! It is insane to think this, but I wanted that medal! With nothing left in the tank, I started sprinting with everything I had. I was slowly gaining on the last six runners. I passed number six, then number five. One hundred yards left and four runners I had to pass to get my medal. Down went number four and three and then number two. Now down to just the two of us for 10th place. The other runner saw me approaching and started sprinting also. We were now running side by side. Who had the will to finish first. Unfortunately, we both did. Ten yards from the finish line there was nothing left. All I could do was stay on my feet. As we got to the finish line I lunged forward and fell to the ground and crumpled up with stomach cramps. My coach and another coach pulled me off the course and helped me stand up. I looked in my coaches' eyes and asked did I finished 10th? When he looked back at me and gave me a nod of the head, that was one of the most rewarding days I have experienced on the athletic field. I had no business finishing in the medal category. I finished 10th! Amazing. I was a winner on this day because I am a scrapper and refused to give into my pain. This was one of the most painful rewards I have received. For 10th place!

One other story gave me a boost this past week. Again, while I was in high school. The Olympics were in Mexico, and the Olympic torch was passing through Oklahoma on its way to Mexico. All the cross-country runners from each of the Tulsa schools were asked if they wanted to run through the night and carry the torch to the Texas border and hand it off to Texas runners. Of course, I volunteered. At midnight, we loaded up in the back of three station wagons and rotated every mile with a different person carrying the torch. We did this all night long. On my sixth rotation and sixth mile, I was carrying the torch, and it went out. What? The eternal flame went out while I was carrying it. All I could think about was the headlines the next day, Tulsa northside kid lets the "Eternal Olympic Flame" go out! I couldn't believe it. However, one of the sponsors settled me down and said this happens occasionally and got it working again. I was so relieved.

As the night wore down and the sun was starting to rise in the east, most of the runners were tired or sleeping and didn't want to carry it any longer. We had four miles to the border. I am a finisher, so I volunteered to run the last four miles. I was tired too, but I was bound and determined to finish at the border. So, again with my stubborn determination, I was able to carry the torch to the Texas border and hand it off to the Texas runners. All total I had the honor of carrying the Olympic torch 10 miles. The effort to run all night across Oklahoma sharing in carrying the Olympic torch was a great honor, and one I will never forget. Why, because it was the Olympic torch, but most of all I was determined to cross the finish line.

So, this week I needed a little talk to myself to keep on fighting, no matter the pain and struggles behind and still ahead, you must finish. But, knowing I have so many people going through the same thing and some in much worse situations, and knowing we all have so many support-ing and praying for us, all the pain is worth it. When we cross the finish line, the reward will be that much more satisfying. Thank you to everyone for just being you and cheering all of us on to finish!

Everyone wants to finish first. Whatever the competition, be it standing up for what you believe, running a race, playing a game, being on a team, we have a natural desire to be first. Why is that? Partly because we have a desire to win, and we are competitive. However, does it mean we have to finish first to be a winner? No. Knowing you competed, gave it your best, and played by the rules, that is how you win. In our society today, it appears it is more important to win than how we won. Just win, Baby! But is that what we want? Is that what we need to give ourselves self-worth?

I am a competitor and love to compete. I am driven to win. That is my motivation. Not because of the recognition it may or may not bring, but because it is a game. Have you ever played a game that did not have an eventual winner? Cards, monopoly, dominoes there is a winner at the end of the game. But, that doesn't mean there has to be a loser. Yes, the scoreboard may show you finished second or even last, but that does not mean you are a loser. If you gave it all you have, then you "won". I finished tenth in my city cross-country race. I did not finish first, but that was one of my most favorite moments in competition. I had nothing left to give, and I finished the race.

How about the game of cancer? That is my biggest game and I have to compete and give it my all. If I lose, well we know what that consequence will be. Will there be obstacles and adversity in this competition? Absolutely! Can I do it alone? Absolutely not!

Yes, there are several games played by just you and your opponent. You have more control of the outcome than team sports. But even in those sports, you usually have a coach or parents that help you develop your skills and challenge you to be better. When things aren't going your way, there is always someone or a contingent of fans pulling for you and encouraging you to reach deep and give it your all.

I will always remember, when I was running a long-distance race, I would reach a point in the race that everything in my body said this is it. I have nothing left to give. We must stop right now. I called it "the wall". But you must push through "the wall", and once you do, in some miraculous way, your mind tells your body quitting is not an option, so let's finish the race. The body responds, and you get a new burst of energy, and now you can run all day long.

When life throws us a curve ball or an obstacle in our way, we must dig in and give it our all to face the challenge. Will it be hard? Probably. Can I do it alone? Probably not! Will I reach a point in my challenge that I have to face "the wall"? Absolutely! Then, it will be decision time. Do I quit or keep fighting? That is an easy one. You keep fighting! Will it be easy? No. But reach out to your support system and let them help you push through "the wall". Once you do that, you will be surprised how much easier it will be the next time you face adversity, and you will just push right through it knowing you can do this.

They always say, "adversity and challenges build character". I really believe this. You will become a better person. You will be prepared for the next obstacle that comes your way. You will know you can finish. You will be a winner.

In the Bible, Paul penned these famous words that we should strive to live by, "I have fought the good fight, I finished the race, I have kept the faith".

20

Journal Entry October 18, 2022 – Taste Buds

A few updates....before we get into those, again, remember our "un-named foxhole friends". We have several going through various stages of cancer treatments and other illnesses.

Ed Stephenson and Brian remembering Brian's days of playing baseball for TU

Brian Humphrey....a few of us visited Brian in the hospital last week. Ken Knight, Bruce Humphrey, Roger Adams, and I were there at the same time. He was much better the day we got there. Brian is now out of the hospital and back at the Cottages. However, in addition to the aspirational pneumonia that put him in the hospital, he has contracted COVID and has UTI. So, no visitors until probably next week.

Larry Byrd....does it ever end! Larry just got out of the hospital after experiencing pneumonia again. He is home trying to regain his strength. While in the hospital, they discovered another health issue. I know Larry is so tired of this never-ending battle with one thing after another. He needs something positive to happen and free him up with these unbelievable health issues.

Another trip to the hospital for Larry

As for me....Like so many of us going through chemo treatments, it is a long and grueling process. You never feel normal, even on your good days. You lose all sense of taste. What I would give for one meal that tastes good. And, you are always weak and tired. But, that is the consequence of chemo. It saves lives, but the process is not enjoyable. I have completed 6 treatments with two to go before the Whipple surgery. On Wednesday, I will have number 7, which will be 11 hours in the chair. I am the first person to arrive when they open the doors, and the last person to leave when they close. Oh well, it is working.

I constantly remind myself, this is a long journey, so be patient and remember winning isn't easy. On the positive side, I am trying on my good days to get out and build up my energy and get in shape I need for the surgery. Last week, Mark Weber and John Phillips took me to Skiatook Lake in Mark's pontoon boat. Not a good day for fishing, but I was able to snag a couple. Just being on the lake was amazing. Then this week, I tried playing golf again after my last outing of having to quit after one hole. This time I played with Roger Adams, Tom Jenkins, Ken Knight, and Steve Caves. I was able to play 15 holes before having to give it up. So, progress! I plan to play in the Letterwinners golf tournament on October 28, so hoping I can last all 18 holes. Just getting out and doing stuff is great for the mind and the body. I hope to see some of you at the tournament.

Well, that is the latest. Several of us are going on our own special journeys. I pray that each of us meet at the end and can celebrate happy endings and many more wonderful years with our families and friends. Have a great week! And, thank you for your support and prayers!!!

One thing I have learned as I continue my journey, whenever I don't feel good or experience another side effect of chemo treatments, all I must do is remember a few of my best friends that have it worse than I do. This puts my problems in perspective and makes me realize it could be worse.

I mentioned earlier the problems I had with the hiccups. That was probably the most difficult side effect I had experienced to this point. Now, I am losing my sense of taste. It is normal to lose your taste buds. I love to eat and especially food with lots of different flavors. But, now I can't taste the food. It all tastes the same and breads taste like cardboard. But, I am assured they will return several weeks after the chemo treatments are done. I am already looking forward to enjoying a full plate of spicy spaghetti.

Each week I am getting closer to being able to have the Whipple surgery and be done with the chemo treatments. Although I am weak from the chemo treatments, I must force myself to keep my strength up so I can manage the long and difficult surgery coming up. I love to fish, and I own a boat. But, I have not been able to get out on the lake for several months. So, two of my friends took me to the lake. Just being on the lake and feeling the cool breeze on my face was magnificent.

The journey is a long one with twists and turns. Just when you fight through one obstacle, another one will pop up around the next corner. At this point in the journey, the end is nowhere in sight. The most difficult days are ahead. Feeling tired and sick is part of the journey. I must continue to be patient and keep my head up as I take it one step at a time. There are no shortcuts to finishing the journey.

I had several friends and several "unnamed" friends going through the same difficulties or even worse. If you think you are having it tough, just look around, and I am sure you will find someone in your life that is having a tougher time than you.

Look on the positive side. Even though the journey is difficult, don't give up on yourself. Believe you can do this. There will be brighter days ahead. But most of all, let hope in, and let it lead the way.

Believe in yourself and let hope in

21

Journal Entry November 4, 2022 – Chemo phase is over, next the Whipple surgery

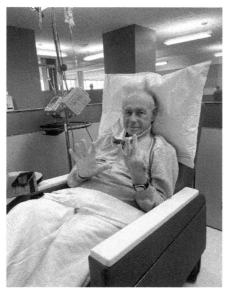

I finally completed my eighth chemo treatment

Well, I hit a milestone yesterday, completing my eighth chemo treatment. This is my last treatment before the Whipple surgery. I need 4-6 weeks to get the chemo out of my system before I can have the surgery. I am glad to get a pause from pumping poison chemo into my body. However, it does save lives, so it is something you must do if you are lucky enough to have the option. Next steps, I will get another CT scan, and then meet with the surgeon on November 21 to go over in greater detail about the Whipple surgery and plan the date, for most likely mid-December. So, thank you again for the unbelievable number of prayers and support. I am truly blessed to experience the love and support. The one big thing I look forward to since chemo is over until after the surgery is the simple pleasure of sitting down and being able to taste a meal. The taste buds should return in about 4 weeks. I can't wait! Hmmm, what should that meal be? I know one thing; it will be a meal full of flavor and maybe a touch of spice.

The first phase of my journey is finally over. I have looked forward to this juncture of the path for several weeks. First, I get a reprieve from the chemo treatments, but most importantly I get to move to the next phase of getting rid of the cancer. Yes, it is one of the most dangerous and a very long surgery of over 8 hours, but this was my only hope to get better.

I needed a pause in my journey to let my body recover from the chemo treatments and get enough strength back to handle the surgery. I had already lost over 20 pounds and expected to lose another 20 pounds after the surgery. But most importantly, my spirits were good. Sure, I was anxious about the surgery because those odds of survival were still in the back of my mind. But, I was ready. The first thing on my mind was getting my taste buds back so I could enjoy a flavorful plate of spaghetti.

When you are facing the most difficult part of the challenges in your lives, this is the time to reach deep into your soul and call upon your faith. Keep a positive spirit that you can do this. God is the light of the world. Trust Him to shine his light through the dark

I was looking forward to a big bowl of spaghetti

clouds and dark forest. Let Him hold your right hand and give you peace about the unknown turns in the path up ahead.

22

Journal Entry November 6, 2022 – Waiting to Score

As I last reported, I have finished 8 rounds of chemo and now await the most difficult Whipple surgery. So, I am finally moving into what I call the "fix it" phase. Although the surgery is very long (could be 8-10 hours) and highly specialized, it is the only hope people with Pancreatic cancer have of surviving the cancer and buying a few more years. I am very blessed to qualify for the surgery because of the stage and location where my cancer sits on the Pancreas. So, I am ready for the challenge and will give it all the fight I have in me. It is easy for me to say this because of all the support and prayers you continue to pass my way.

When I found out I had cancer and it was pancreatic cancer, lots of things go through your mind. Of course, am I going to die is one of the first thoughts. It is unavoidable. But, the second thought was the most important to me. How am I going to deal with this? After hugging my wife and listening to her talk and comforting me, I felt better, but still unsure. I have shared with you that the next morning of a restless night of trying to sleep, the first line in my morning devotional reading, God said, "give me your right hand and I will take care of you." With tears in my eyes, that was the answer to how I was going to deal with this. I have had peace ever since that moment. God didn't say he would heal me, he said I will take care of you! Is that the same? I pray it is, but it is what it is! Whatever the outcome, I am truly blessed to take this journey. I am such a better person, I hope, from this journey. I know one thing; I have experienced all the good in this world from amazing people that love and care for each other. I have received so much strength from those of you that have already been down this journey. I can never thank you enough.

Let's set the record straight....I am just an ordinary guy that is one of millions of others carrying around cancer in their body. Including several of our "unnamed fox hole friends". I am not special or deserve anything more than you would give anyone else.

I decided to share my journey when I told my kids and extended family, I will be transparent in my journey, if they can handle the twists and turns and ups and downs that go with something like this. It has not been easy to share the quiet doubting moments or the days when the chemo has really kicked my butt. But, what I have found is that it has given me internal therapy and based upon the feedback, so many of you have appreciated riding along with me. If anything can come out of my transparency and often long-winded stories, maybe it will help someone that may be going through cancer treatments or may someday have to deal with it as well. If I can take some of the mystery and scariness of cancer and make it more real, then it has been worth my ramblings.

So, the last time I shared my journey, I had spent some time sitting on the big boulder under the beautiful, shaded Aspen tree on the side of a long meadow on the side of the mountain reflecting on the journey behind me. I then started the uphill climb towards the darker path that was much more rugged and steeper to climb.

I have finally reached the opening to the dark path. The meadows to the left of me are gone, and the beautiful stream running through the forest has disappeared into the canyon far below me on the right. This time the path before me is uneven, filled with large, pointed rocks and narrow on both sides. Huge drop-offs on both sides are waiting to send you over and down the mountain with any wrong misstep. Little bits of sunlight filter through some of the trees, just enough to let you see a few yards in front of you. As difficult as it seems to climb this last path, there is no other way around it. To reach the other end, and hopefully, the end of the journey, you must keep going forward with faith that you can and will make it. This is where I am today. As I await my next phase and the surgery, there is no other way to finish the race. I will do it, and I will make it! Not because of my doings, but because of the prayers and support I receive every day!

So, where is my mind wandering today? What life experiences have I lived that give me the strength to push forward into the unknown future. There is so much swirling around, but then I look to my left into a somewhat misty haze. I see the form of a dugout. In the corner of the dugout is Coach Shell. Next to him is my dad. What is he doing in the dugout? I know they are in Heaven, but they don't appear to be giving me the wave home to join them. Instead, they are shouting words of encouragement and telling me to be strong and fight. Then, I see all my teammates and friends standing on the top step of the dugout. Some shouting my name with encouragement and others waving towels of support. This is the bottom of the ninth and the score is tied. I am the leadoff hitter, and I know this time I will not be able to foul off the curves and wait for my favorite fastball pitch. I have always had trouble with the right-handed sidearm slider that just sweeps across the plate and out of the strike zone. But this time, I must hit this wicked pitch to get on base. I know Tom Jenkins is hitting behind me and will get the hit to move me into scoring position on second base.

Tom did as he said and got a base hit. I am the winning run, and I am standing on second base. Waiting for another of my teammates, Phil Honeycutt, to drive me home. This time I am not kidding, I need Buckets to do what he always does, and get the hit so I can score. I glance into the dugout and see all the support and encouragement coming from my teammates. I see Coach Shell standing in the third base coaches' box, waiting to wave me home. Then I see Dad, still standing in the corner of the dugout, but now on the top step as well. He is just looking at me and giving me that look, "you can do it Son". It's time to beat this cancer and cross home plate.

As I am standing on second base, Phil is digging in at home plate. The pitcher is making his windup and delivering the ball to home. Phil is waiting on the pitch....Just then my mind comes back to reality. The sight of the misty dugout is gone, and I am just standing in the middle of the dark damp path. However, I can see the end of the path several yards away. I know I can reach the end, just keep pushing. But, what happens next is totally out of my control. I have my faith to lean on, which has been with me all the way. I have so many friends and teammates praying and supporting me and giving me so much comfort and peace. I can never thank you enough for this life-changing journey. I am truly BLESSED!

So, now, in a few weeks I will meet with the surgeon. I have prayed for God to give me the right surgeon for the surgery. It is not easy, and you never know if you did the right thing. But my brother told me "You can have the best surgeon in the world, but if it is time for you to go home, then you will go home. However, if you have the worst surgeon in the world and it isn't time to go home yet, then you won't go home." That settled it for me. I have the right surgeon for the job, but it is not in my control. I have my faith; I have my family, and I have my friends! And I have Phil Honeycutt standing at home waiting for the pitch to drive me home and celebrate several more years of life on this beautiful earth!

Now that the next phase is ahead of me, I am ready to cross home plate and score the winning run. But as I have said several times, the results of my journey are out of my control. I need help. I have needed the prayers and support from the hundreds now following my journey. I have needed the proper plan and execution of the plan as laid out by my oncologist, Dr. Scott Cole, his staff, and all the nurses in the chemotherapy rooms administering the proper "cocktail" for my cancer. Now I need the help and the expertise of my surgeon, Dr. Edward Cho and his staff. But most of all, I need God to take care of me when He said He would hold my right hand.

When you reach that phase of your difficulties and obstacles in your life where you have tried for days, weeks, and maybe months to get through them, you are ready to see the results. You are probably tired physically and emotionally. You have probably been frustrated at times. Now you are anxious to see the results of your efforts. But are you really ready for the results? What if the result is not what I wanted or expected? Remember, you are the main character in this journey, but all the unexpected twists and turns were out of your control. However, how you dealt with those adversities was a learning experience and made you a better person. Be thankful and humbled by the support you received as you fought each step of the way.

In my case, my journey was all about dealing with pancreatic cancer. I was fighting for more years of living on this earth with my family and friends. I was humbled and blessed by the outpouring of support.

The journey is not over. However, often when I needed that little boost of support that would calm my anxieties, someone would say something, or I would read something that really gave me peace. This time my brother uttered those words and gave me just what I needed.

"You can have the best surgeon in the world, but if it is time for you to go home, then you will go home. However, if you have the worst surgeon in the world and it isn't time to go home yet, then you won't go home."

Journal Entry November 22, 2022 – Happy Thanksgiving

I wanted to take a moment to wish everyone a Happy Thanksgiving week. Eat lots of turkey and then go take a nap. Also, be sure to remember those special people and moments in your life that you are thankful for. They are the spices of life that give us purpose and happiness.

I am especially thankful and blessed to have such wonderful friends that are always there when I need them. True friends are forever. To my high school, college, baseball, church, fishing, golf, and everyone else I have wonderful relationships, Thank You for your prayers and support. You have no idea how much that means to me and keeps me going.

To my wife, kids, and extended family, thank you for your unconditional love and support. I love you!

So, we still have several friends on our unnamed friends list that still need your prayers and support. They are slowly getting better, and moving forward in their various stages of healing. To each of you on this list, even though you prefer to keep your journeys private, just know that you have a name, and we pray for your healing every day!

Remember, December 19th, Larry Byrd will be having surgery to remove the cancerous tumor in his kidney. I have received so much inspiration and support from Larry and Suzi by them sharing their journeys, and helping me understand my journey in a better way. Also, remember Brian Humphrey, as he is restricted to a bed every day. I have never heard one complaint from Brian. Each time I see Brian, he gives me a shot of inspiration.

As to my journey.....As I mentioned in my last update, I have been slowly walking up this steep, dark, and damp path the last few weeks. I am approaching the end of this path, but I cannot see what is ahead. It appears there should be only one fork in the road. The end of the journey or another path that continues the journey to another stage. Whatever path I am destined to take, I am truly blessed to experience such an amazing journey. I am not worthy of the overwhelming support. You have made me a better person. I hope my journey has helped someone along the way as well as the therapy it has given me.

As I was walking up this more difficult path, I found a four-foot stick that had a curved end. Much like a walking cane. It appeared to have fallen out of a tree and landed on the path, just waiting for me to pick it up. Perfectly shaped and just the right length for me to lean on and have a place to place my arm and rest my chin. There are no smooth boulders on this path and nowhere to rest on the side of the path. So, when I need to rest, I just lean on my walking stick and close my eyes and reflect on my past and what may be up ahead. It is quiet, other than an occasional bird chirping in the treetops or a couple of chipmunks chasing each other among the rocks. Perfect for hearing the stillness of my thoughts and those that God has been sharing with me.

As I look back on the last two weeks, the stage I have been fighting for is now making my journey more real. Raw emotions and anxiety are coming to the surface more often than before. This is it. This is the stuff I read about on the internet, the odds for survival, the difficult recovery. The strain it puts on my family. This is where the prayers and support you have been giving me really pay off. I still have a strong faith and belief that I am going to fight this with all my might, and we are going to beat this thing. My faith is strong. But, I am just a guy with cancer and have the same emotions and anxious moments anyone would have facing the unknown that lies up ahead. Like I have said, winning isn't easy; winning takes a team working together; it requires patience; taking one step at a time. Most importantly, it takes the will to meet the challenge with confidence and belief in yourself and your team, and knowing God has this, just like he told me to "give me your right hand and I will take care of you". It is out of my control. I am at peace!

During the last couple of weeks, I had a CT scan, met with the surgeon and my cardiologist. I have finally come to the point in my journey that I have been anxiously waiting. With chemo behind me for now, I am in the "fix it" stage. The Whipple surgery is such a big surgery. I had to get approval from my cardiologist to determine if my heart could stand up to such a challenge. I met with him today and he gave me the approval to have the surgery. Whew! One obstacle down. I met with my oncologist last week to go over my latest CT scan. Although it wasn't totally conclusive, it appeared the tumor had not grown any larger and from what they could tell from my markers, the cancer has not spread to other organs. But, they won't know until they open me up and see for themselves. I met with the surgeon last week, and he set the date for 7:00am December 8th at St. John's. He explained in detail what to expect. He said I will be in ICU after the surgery and up walking on day two. He expects I will be in the hospital for 5-7 days. He wants me home for Christmas! He told my wife that he will start cutting around 7:00 am, and the surgery should take 4-6 hours, not counting the pre-surgery and post-surgery tasks. Before he makes the long incision down the front of my body, he is going to do a smaller cut so he can scope the insides to confirm what he expects, and that the cancer has not spread. If it has, he will stop the surgery and go no farther. You only get one shot at this. When he told my wife that he would give her frequent updates we were pleased. But, he then said, if you see me in the first hour, that will not be good news. When I heard that, reality really hit home. I held back a tear that wanted to run down my cheek, but I could not avoid the big lump in my throat. All those plans I had for life after surgery faded away momentarily. A real raw moment took over. But, that is ok. Winning isn't easy! Be strong. This is real life!

So, why do I share these raw moments? My journey would not be complete if I wasn't honest and shared only the good parts. When words are shared that can be intimidating, then you have choices. Let them get the best of you or rise above them and fight. My surgeon was just being truthful, which I would not want any other way.

At this point, I would like to make a request to all my friends who have supported me during this journey. We have a small area reserved for just family. They are going to be under a lot of stress watching the time and hoping the surgeon will not come out during the first hour. Also, I will not be in any condition to entertain visitors for a few days. So, the family and I thank you for your support, but request you not come to the hospital for a few days to give all of us time to get through the first few stressful and painful days. Then, I will be in a better place to see you. My family will *update Facebook and send out updates on our email distribution lists to provide you with the latest news. Thank you for how much you mean to me and my family. I hope you understand.*

This brought back to me another instance that history has allowed to become one of my legacy moments. I know, here he goes with another baseball story. As a young boy, all I wanted to do was play baseball. I was lucky to live my dream and live some of the best days of my life. Playing and competing with amazing teammates consisting of players before and after me that we built into one of the greatest programs at TU is a legacy that will never be forgotten. I was even honored to write a book about those days.

But, my one legacy moment is known as the elevator story. I had a choice how to respond to a moment intended to intimidate me. I decided to save my fight for later that evening. For those of you that do not know about the story, here you go. For those of you that have heard it over and over, just skip to the end of the paragraph. In 1969, we were playing Texas that night in the second round of the College World Series. James Street, the Texas All American quarterback and great pitcher, was throwing against us that night. Texas was staying at the same hotel. I got off to a good start in the tournament, getting a couple base hits including the winning hit in the 11th inning against Chris Chambliss and UCLA. Cliff Butcher and I were on the elevator when James Street and another Texas player got on with us. In those days, bantering was normal during the game and could get ugly at times. Street decided to start the bantering early and looked at me and said, "Who are you, the bat boy?" I was furious but decided to not start something in the elevator. But, I never forgot his words. Intimidating, no! But, it brought out my fighting spirit even more! So, in the 5th inning, in a tight game, with two of my teammates on base, I got my revenge and hit a three-run home run off of James Street. Rounding second base, I had a few words for James Street as well. We went on to win the game. James Street recently passed away, but our little battle is still legendary. Jeb Blount, TU quarterback, knows the Street family very well. After Jeb heard about the story, he shared it with James's son, who was also a very good ball player. His son loved the story and wants to meet me someday. Jeb gave him a copy of our TU baseball book. So, it looks like James Street will forever be linked to my little legacy moment.

I told this story because it is one of those moments I can think about when I need a little extra strength to push forward, no matter the words or the challenge, to remind me that with God's help, I can rise above and beat the situation.

This time it is the biggest challenge I have faced. I told you before, if I can get on base and Tom Jenkins gets me in scoring position, then I know Phil Honeycutt will drive me home. I mentioned Coach Shell is standing in the third base coaches' box to wave me home. I also mentioned everyone in the dugout was now standing on the top step pulling for Buckets to get the hit and pulling for me to score. I also saw my dad standing in the corner of the dugout and wondered why he was in the dugout? Well, now I know. I told you I would have to hit the always dangerous and most difficult pitch, the righthanded sidearm slider that sweeps across the plate and out of the strike zone to get on base. As I am taking a few practice swings in the on-deck circle, my dad calls me over and whispers in my ear. He says, "Son, you remember all those days you dreamed of being a ball player and pretended to be the one that won the game? Those days when you would be hitting tennis balls into the neighbor's yard, or the days when we would play with a whiffle ball that had a nasty slider breaking across the plate, and you would hit it like it was a fastball down the middle? Sure do, Dad. So, this is one of those moments you dreamed of on the driveway. It's just real life now. You have so much support pulling for you. But, you have prepared for this moment. You have the right team behind you. Now, you get up there in the box and give it your best fight, and you will win this game. Thanks Dad. I will see you at home plate. Oh, Dad, thanks for being my dad and sitting in the dugout today! We got this!"

Use this week of Thanksgiving to be thankful for what you have been given in this life and how much you make a difference in someone else's life. You sure have made a difference in my life.

Love you all! Happy Thanksgiving!!

Listening to my doctors preparing me on what to expect in the surgery brought a lot of thoughts to my mind. When you are going into a surgery that may have a bad ending you give a pause to everything and think about what you have experienced so far and what the possible world could look like ahead. I will admit, the thoughts of this not ending well were there as well.

I appreciated my doctors being honest with me and telling me and my family what to expect and what could go wrong. This helped us all a lot. Was it easy hearing the different scenarios? No. But I wanted to hear about the good and bad possibilities as well. I knew this was a high-risk surgery and was pleased the doctors admitted it too. But my surgeon said he had done several of these and was not worried. That put me at ease.

Often when we are going through tough times someone, or several people are watching you and how you deal with adversity. Hopefully, we do it the right way and can be a positive example to others. Make a difference in someone else's life.

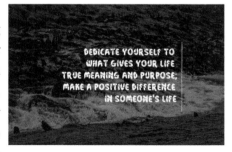

DEDICATE YOURSELF TO
WHAT GIVES YOUR LIFE
TRUE MEANING AND PURPOSE;
MAKE A POSITIVE DIFFERENCE
IN SOMEONE'S LIFE

24 |

Journal Entry December 5, 2022
– Hope Frees Us, Maybe from
Ourselves

Hi everyone,

I wanted to give an update on my journey before Thursday's surgery. I won't be physically able to send updates for a while after surgery, so I am sending it out now. My family is going to send out a Facebook and email list updates after the surgery.

This has been quite a ride over the last few months. But I found peace with it all early in the process. That, and your unbelievable support have lightened the impact of the bad days. Until you walk through something like this you cannot imagine the impact support and prayers can have on a person. You are amazing. I thank you from the bottom of my heart. I also thank you for the support and prayers you have given our unnamed foxhole friends. They are so blessed by the support you have given them.

Don't forget to remember Larry Byrd, as he has another cancer surgery on December 19th. Larry and Suzi have been through so much, but they always have time to call and pray for me. Their experiences and words have been so helpful to me. They inspire me to keep pushing forward.

So many of you have been through similar journeys and your positive attitudes inspire us all. Thank you! Lastly, I want everyone to know how much Brian Humphrey has "given me a shot of inspiration" every time I visit him. He is concerned about me and while lying on his back in a bed paralyzed, he still prays for me. I wish I was as strong and caring as he. I told him it will be several weeks before I get to see him again, so I am hoping some of you can give him a visit. Tell him I love him.

One last comment before I continue with my thoughts and my journey. I know I am very wordy, and you could break my sentences into three sentences. But, sharing my journey and the often-crazy stories that I interject into my updates has been a source of therapy for me. I guess I am a story-teller and a dreamer, but I do enjoy it. I have often thought of quitting the long updates, but so many friends have encouraged me to continue. So, I hope that means I am at least sharing something you have enjoyed and found valuable to you. So, with that being said, I left two stories unfinished that I must finish. The first was my trek on the dark and damp path to who knows what is ahead. The second story I had Phil Honeycutt at home plate waiting on a pitch so he could bring me home with a game winning hit. I hope they have happy endings. Here we go....

As they say, game day is almost here. That's what it feels like to me. I am often asked are you getting anxious about the surgery? Let's put it this way, yes, it is on my mind all the time now that it is getting close. Mostly, what do I need to get done before the surgery that I can't do after surgery. With Christmas coming soon, I need to take care of my Christmas shopping this week. Last week, my wife and I bought Georgie and Teddy a basketball goal for Christmas. Since I had to put it together and had nowhere to store it, I enlisted the help of my brother Rick to help me assemble the goal. It said it takes about one to two hours to assemble. However, don't believe it. After four hours and now in the dark, we finally got it finished.

Since we assembled it in their backyard, Georgie and Teddy got an early Christmas gift. They love it! They better!

Rather than anxious, I guess it feels more like getting butterflies in your stomach before the game. I have no fear of the outcome. However, I do know and am fully aware of all the possibilities. But I am at peace. My wife received a prayer this past week from one of her dear friends. I asked if I could have a copy. It is perfect for where I am on my journey. It goes like this... **"We can let go; we can trust in what will be. Not that it's perfect or simple or even soon, but that it's not all up to us. HOPE frees us, maybe from ourselves."**

One thought that seems to never go away is the thought when I am laying in the bed ready to be wheeled away to surgery and I look into the eyes of my wife and kids and tell them bye and I love them, will this be the last time I see them? Is this the final goodbye? Not trying to be dramatic, but these are real thoughts and emotions when going into "big surgeries". At least for me. But as I have said from the beginning, "it is what it is". And I plan on seeing them again in a few hours after surgery.

One other item I marked off the list before surgery. The day finally came when I got enough of my taste buds back. I ordered a 12-ounce Ribeye steak. It covered the entire plate. My wife saw the steak and how big it was and asked if I was going to eat that whole thing. My response, "absolutely, and going to enjoy every juicy bite". Man, it was good! Oh, the little pleasures of life.

Regarding the surgery and where is my mind. Besides wondering where I am going to wake up, you catch yourself lingering on the negative possibilities. Such things as wills, living wills, advanced directives to ensure those things are up to date. Yes, the thoughts of funerals are on the list too. Not that I expect the worst-case scenario, but you do have to consider those issues as well. It comes with the territory of having cancer and any other life-threatening illness. But I have not let it get me down, but rather treat it as getting ready for another meeting and here is the agenda. Don't be afraid to talk about it with your family. It doesn't have to be a heavy mournful subject. Nor that it is the expected outcome. For me, since it is an option, I decided to address it head on.

The other side of the coin, the positive thoughts. One day when my youngest daughter, Cathleen, was sitting with me during my chemo session, we started talking about things I enjoyed growing up. My favorite was going to Yellowstone every year. So, Cathleen and I decided to plan a trip to Yellowstone in an RV and create a memory Georgie and Teddy could enjoy. I didn't own an RV. So, I talked to my brother, and we decided to buy an RV that all our families could enjoy and create memories. So, we now have an RV! How is that for planning on getting well and back on my feet in a few months? I am planning to travel to Yellowstone and of course get back on the river and do more fly fishing!

So, back to my journey. I have finally reached the part of the journey for which I have been waiting. I cannot get well without this next phase. This is the game changer phase of the journey. Since I don't know the outcome of the surgery, as the prayer said, "we can trust in what will be and Hope frees us maybe from ourselves". I am going to share what I believe will be the outcome.

We left off on my journey walking up the difficult and treacherous dark and damp path. I finally reached the top of the path, expecting at least two paths to travel. One going off to the right where the journey ends. The other path branching off to the left where the journey continues. Under what conditions I did not know. But, I looked around

and there were no paths for me to travel. I just stood at the top of the mountain with darkness behind me and nothing but heavenly beauty in front of me. It wasn't heaven, but it reminded me of heaven. All around me, as far as I could see, were open meadows full of amazing colors of flowers that blanketed the ground under the beautiful clear blue skies. The flowers were so thick and knee high tall that I could not see the ground or where I should walk. Off to the right and down to the valley below, the stream appeared again. This time it is moving slowly and spreading out into a flooded meadow. As I was looking at the flooded meadow, I noticed a beaver's dam was being built by a family of beavers. A muskrat was standing nearby watching the beavers working so hard to build a dam. In the flooded meadow were a couple of moose with their noses poking deep in the water. They were enjoying themselves on the fresh roots of the grass all around them. Then I saw several chipmunks playing among the boulders and dead wood laying on the banks of the now small pond. It was a beautiful and peaceful sight.

As my eyes shifted back to the flowered meadow and watching it continue down the mountain and up the side of another mountain before me, I noticed quite a bit of commotion going on in the valley way below me. It looked like people getting ready for a party or celebration of some sort. As I began to focus on the people, I could now recognize my wife and kids and extended family were part of the crowd. Several others were arriving and joining in on the preparations. They all seemed so happy. Now I could make out their faces. It was all my prayer warriors, foxhole friends and several others that had been praying for me and giving me so much support. There were our unnamed foxhole friends, but this time they were not sick but very healthy and full of joy. Even Brian Humphrey was there. The person that was paralyzed and never complained about his

situation. The person that always gave me a shot of inspiration. However, he was sitting up in a wheelchair. He was surrounded by several of his friends as well.

Then I felt the hand of another holding my right hand. I looked up and God said, "remember that first morning when you found out you had pancreatic cancer, I said give me your right hand and I will take care of you? Well, I have never let go. Let's sit here among the flowers and reflect on your journey. It isn't over, but it is time to rest a bit before your surgery". I looked at God and asked why all the preparations for a party? It looks like a celebration of some sort. Am I going to die? Is this the preparation for my Celebration of Life? But they look so happy. I don't understand. Do they know we are up here? So many questions. God said "you know I cannot not tell you the future and what will happen. You would not be able to handle knowing the future. That is a job that only me and my angels. If I shared with you the future, then mankind would think they have control and would not need me any longer. Can you imagine what that world would look like?"

"Let's talk about that vision you had. The vision of you playing the last inning of a ballgame determined the outcome of your journey. Remember? You had to hit your most difficult pitch to get on base. I also stepped into the batter's box with you and then you hit a line drive base hit. Then, Tom Jenkins got a base hit and moved you to second base. He had the help of your family standing in the batter's box with him. You were now in scoring position. All you needed was Phil Honeycutt to get a base hit and drive you home with the winning run.

As Phil was approaching the batter's box, the other team made a pitching change. They brought in the toughest relief pitcher in the league. His nickname was "Big C". He had pitches that often-sent hitters back to the bench with a strike out. He had pitches that were so difficult to hit that you didn't even know he had made the pitch. Before he even had a chance to swing, Phil had two strikes on him. He never saw the pitch. Phil did not match up well with this guy. But, we had a secret weapon on our team as well. He had the whole team on his side. The team was standing on the top step of the dugout, but now they left the dugout and stood beside Phil. Advantage our team.

With all this support behind him, and two strikes on Phil, he lined the next pitch into the left centerfield gap for a base hit. As you took off to third base, Coach Shell was waving you home to score the winning run. It should not be a problem to score since the ball ran all the way to the out-field wall. Then you stopped running and froze in place halfway between third base and home plate. Tom Jenkins, running behind you, ready to help you up if you stumbled and fell while sprinting to home plate, had to stop as well. Your teammates just froze and stopped cheering a sure thing winning score. What is going on? Doesn't he want to win the game? We have come this far, fighting through lots of adversity and he is giving up? Now? After everyone cheering you on through this whole battle? Then, I will never forget what happened next. As I was running along beside you. I had stopped as well. Then, you looked up at me with a look that needed my approval. I knew immediately what you were thinking. With a grin on my face, I gave you a nod of approval. You deserve this little moment. Then you began running as fast as you could towards home plate. Rather than take the easy path and running through and stepping on home plate, just before you reached home plate you lunged forward in a headfirst slide. After the big cloud of dust had settled, there you were, sitting on home plate just covered with dirt over your entire uniform. You looked up at me with this big sheepish grin, while enjoying your dirty uniform. Then to all your teammates you declared to everyone that could hear, "with everyone's support and especially God holding my right hand, "Dirty old Ballplayers" never quit until the game is won. Winning isn't easy, one step at a time, be patient, it takes the entire team pulling for each other. Today, with the help of everyone, I touched home plate!"

As we laughed at my crazy vision, it was the underlining truth of that vision that meant the most to me. The one that brought me to this point in my journey looking forward with **Hope that frees us, even from ourselves.** That hope was given to me because of the love and support I have received along my journey. I could not have gotten this far by myself. When I say, I am blessed to travel this journey and I am a better person because of it, it is those of you that prayed and supported me every step of the way that gave me this experience. It is the unnamed foxhole friends that gave me the honor of sharing in their journeys and knowing every prayer and support I received, was also being shared upon them as well. It is the faith and believing that God will hold your right hand and take care of you each step of the way.

As we turned our thoughts back to the preparations of a celebration taking place in the valley below, God looks at me and says, "Yes this is a celebration. Remember when you said at the beginning of your journey that you couldn't decide if you should share your journey in a public way? You asked me to never let this journey be about you. But, let your journey be useful in some way as you travel the unknown along the way. As you prayed to me daily for strength, you also constantly reminded me it isn't about you, but your journey. I decided we needed to celebrate today by honoring everyone that took the extra step and had faith in praying and supporting you along the way. When I receive so many prayers and love being shared for one purpose, I listen. If that purpose recognizes my power and helps others as well, I will answer those prayers. Your purpose has brought the best out of people. Even those that are fighting serious illness as well. You are very fortunate to have so many wonderful friends and family. You really are blessed. I am happy to answer their prayers. Now, I have a request. We have known each other since you were eight years old. I have always referred to you as

Roger. You have said your friends and teammates call you "Whit". Is that ok with you that I call you "Whit" from now on? I want all your friends and those that support you to know that I am part of the team."

As our focus returns to the valley below, it is about time to join my friends and family. They haven't seen me sitting on the top of the mountain looking down at them. I can't wait. We have lots to celebrate while I honor their support. I feel brave and that I can ask God for a favor at any time. All he can say is not this time. But, I lean over to him and whisper a request in his ear, even for just one day, I ask. He smiles and says, "since you asked and this is a day to celebrate," he just turns his head to the valley below and gives his whole mind and power to one person. I turn my head to this one person also. As I do, I watch my friend Brian Humphrey, who gives me inspiration every day, rise out of his wheelchair and stand beside it. He looks up the mountain and we lock eyes. Then, we give each other our customary thumbs up followed by a fist bump. Then, I know he can hear my thoughts and I let him know, "Brian, one day, because of your love and faith, you will be made whole again. I love you brother."

Wow, what a journey I have been blessed to travel. I know this isn't the end of the road. Whatever the outcome, I want my immediate and extended family to know that this was a journey we traveled together every day. It was difficult at times, but I always knew you were there for me. To my kids, Ryan, Barbe, and Cathleen; my 95-year-old mom, Norma; my brother Rick and sister-in-law, Cathy, you all wanted to go on the ride and face all the ups, downs, twists, and turns. You were amazing in always understanding and giving me the love and support I needed. As to my wife, you were there for me every day and night. You never got to rest. You had to endure my bad days and mood changes. You had to comfort me when I needed to be comforted. You had to put up with my forgetting things because of my chemo brain. You had to be the steady hand when I was wobbly in thought and step. I cannot thank you enough.

To everyone....You make me a better person. Your support allowed me to arrive at this point of this amazing journey. I love you all! I hope to see you in the next few days, weeks, and months....Whit

Was I at the end of my journey? It seemed all paths of my journey led to the day I would have the Whipple surgery. The outcome of the surgery would determine what my next path would be like or maybe there would not be another path. It was out of my control.

God held my hand the entire journey, and still was holding tight. He knew I really needed it now. This was a big surgery and a long recovery. Did I think the surgery might not go well and this was the end of the journey? Sure, those thoughts crossed my mind. I guess I wouldn't be normal if they didn't. However, I was at peace with whatever the outcome.

What happened next was unplanned and a total surprise to me. Earlier in my journey after several weeks and months of going through the chemo treatments and the side effects, I needed to take a pause. I climbed up on the boulder and had wonderful moments of reflection of what I had traveled and experienced from the day I found out I had cancer. The decision to write my journals was huge for me. Not only was it tremendous therapy and got me acknowledging my true thoughts and raw moments, but going public with my journals and the response was off the charts. It is this experience of prayers and support that made me appreciate how much my friends and even those you don't know can mean to you going through the struggles of fighting cancer. Then on top of that meeting and trusting the doctors, their staff and the nurses in the chemotherapy rooms is just an amazing experience. If I never had cancer, I would not have had these experiences. This is why I say I am blessed to have traveled this journey. Whatever happens next doesn't matter. I have been blessed in so many ways.

The best part of this journey was watching and receiving the benefits of walking everyday with God in a closer and more personal way. Experiencing firsthand how God answers prayer and then holds your hand to give you peace is just, well heavenly. This is why I say, when you are faced with difficulties in your life, you cannot solve them by yourself. You need that special friend; you need to ask God to help you and let Him hold your hand. Then, you must be willing to be patient by taking it one step at a time and tell yourself no matter how difficult the adversity, you will not quit.

As I was coming out of the difficult rocky and dark path I had been traveling, I guess God thought I needed another pause. This time not looking back in moments of reflection, but this time appreciating how the journey has changed my life and how much goodness is still in this world. I am just an ordinary guy that has cancer, just like so many others before me. But, wow, what an experience.

I really believe the experiences you go through from a small child to a grown adult form your character and passion in life. From all those days playing pretend baseball games with my brother on the driveway hitting tennis balls or playing whiffle ball instilled in me the passion and focus to get a college scholarship to play baseball. I learned how to compete, even with myself. I learned from playing sports the importance of having teammates all pulling together to win the game. I learned that no matter the score, if you have one out left, you can still win the game. I learned to never quit, no matter how big the adversity. But most of all I learned that I needed God helping me to develop the skills and passion to accomplish my dreams. As I walked the paths of my journey, I had to call upon all these past experiences and developed character traits to make it this far.

God knew as I came out of the dark passageways of the paths I had traveled, I needed time to rest before going further into another difficult phase. There were some tough difficulties ahead that I could never anticipate. That is why He only reveals to us what we need to know now.

In my mind's eye, I could see a celebration in the valley below. A celebration including all the people that had traveled the journey with me. It was not a celebration that I was healed. It was a celebration of how "letting hope in, frees us even from ourselves."

What is our first reaction when faced with an obstacle or difficulty in our lives? If you are like me, you kick into "fix it" mode. I can or must solve this problem. "Listen to me, this is how we are going to fix this problem." Well, I cannot count the number of times I start fixing a problem and find out I can't do it after all. I don't have the right tools or knowledge to finish the job. Then, I must call the expert to come bail me out of my mess and take over. I continue to make the same mistakes repeatedly. I think I have control and can fix anything. But, if I was smart, I would ask for help and let the person that has the expertise fix it in the beginning.

Life's problems need experts to help us. There is no greater expert than God. So, call upon Him first to solve it for us or let Him have control to lead us. God used all my friends to help me. So, it is time to be thankful for their prayers and support and celebrate their efforts. It is also time for me to realize how blessed I am to have traveled this journey.

"We can let go; we can trust in what will be. Not that it's perfect or simple or even soon, but that it's not all up to us. HOPE frees us, maybe from ourselves."

25

Journal Entry December 7 and 19, 2022 – Whipple Surgery – A Big Blow to the Body

December 7, 2022

It's just a few hours until one of the most important days of my life. The phone calls, texts, Facebook comments, and email support have been amazing today. Just know I appreciate everything you have done for me. I am truly blessed. I love you all! We got this! See you soon.

December 19, 2022

Just got word from Suzi Byrd. The doctor said he removed Larry's cancerous mass and a cyst. Everything looks great! They thank you for your prayers. He will be in the hospital for 2-3 days.

Hi everyone. It feels wonderful to feel good enough to sit at my laptop and reach out to my friends and supporters again. I feel like I have been through so much since surgery that I don't know where to begin. But first, please take a few moments and pray for Larry Byrd today as he is having surgery on his kidney. Also, pray for our unnamed foxhole friends as well. Since I have been out of it for the last several days, I have lost contact with their latest status. But I will get a more current report in the next few days.

I also want to thank my brother Rick and a few others that have given you updates occasionally. He is such a great brother. Also let me tell you how much I love you and how your support and prayers have given me more time to spend in this beautiful world with you and my family. I can't express it sufficiently, but it comes deep within the core of my body.

When I woke up from surgery in the ICU room, the first people I saw were my wife, kids, and family. Their smiles told me everything I needed to hear. I don't remember if the tears were flowing down my cheeks, but they sure were on the insides of my now cut-up body. My journey continues. Whatever that is.

Boy, did I find out quickly what the next few days and weeks of the journey would be like. I am only 8 days from surgery, but as much as I did not like Chemo, I will gladly take chemo over these past few days. I will have four more rounds of chemo starting in February. So, where am I now? What lies ahead?

The first thing I have learned, as I have always said, is that I am just another regular guy that has cancer. Yes, I am a fighter, and I have my faith. But I had no control over the outcome! You are the ones that had control over the outcome!! When I am sitting there listening to the doctor tell me what he found when he opened me up and what transpired as he sewed me up, I could not control my emotions. I was doing my best to not lose control, but my eyes started tearing up, my jaw started quivering, and my body shaking. He said the tumor had shrunk to a very small size, he got the cancer that he could see and that he sent the lymph nodes to the labs to be tested but did not see any cancer there either.

It wasn't just the results that made me so emotional. My mind went directly to each of you that had taken the time to give me support, phone calls, texts, and prayers, and that they had been answered. Me, "Whit", just another guy, a "dirty old ballplayer" you cared enough for me to make a difference. So many of you don't even know me but you decided to pray as well.

We often think about what we can do to leave our mark on this earth that made a difference. You can check that box off the list. It's not so much for me, but you proved God answers prayer and you put your faith to the test in a very big way. Thank you for that. That is why I was so emotional. I was the beneficiary.

As we left my journey before surgery, I was coming down the beautiful flowery mountain to join you in the valley for a celebration in your honor. As I came out of surgery, I was no longer in the valley, but on top of the mountain on the other side of the valley. I could see the beautiful Ocean with its calm emerald, blue waters several thousand feet below and a couple miles in the distance. God still had a hold of my right hand and on my left were my wife, kids, and extended family. But the mountain floor was covered in a dark black layer of lava flow left over from a volcano eruption hundreds of years ago. To reach the end of my journey, I must walk over this lava flow. Each step is and will be painful and full of pointed shards of stone

waiting to punch a hole in your skin. This will take difficult steps and several weeks to get to the Ocean. When I fall, my wife and kids would remind me how difficult this will be, but you must do it. There is only one way. One step at a time. Sometimes baby steps. So, I continue my journey.

Since surgery, I spent seven days in the hospital. Lots of pain, no appetite, forcing down distasteful nutritional drinks. Often those drinks full of the calories I needed to get better would come back up within the next few hours. Net gain, zero. I even hit depression levels and insisted the doctors let me go home. Which they finally did. I am now going through the same things at home, without depression. With the help of my wife and kids, I am slowly getting through each day and getting better. The doctor said he did one of the most difficult surgeries and gave me a big "body blow." He said I should be much better in two weeks and back to normal in two months. I can tell improvement each day. But this has put a hardship on my wife and the family as they try to help. Yesterday, I had to watch the ambulance take my wife to the hospital from pure exhaustion. Please pray for her as well. As I continue to gain strength each day, I am more open to visits and phone calls.

So, in closing, thank you again for your faith in prayer giving me many more days and years on this earth. I am truly blessed.

I plan to spend Christmas with my family and enjoy every minute of it. Have a Merry Christmas and a Happy New Year!!

I love each and every one of you....Whit

When I said my goodbyes to my family as I was being wheeled into the surgery room, I really did not know where I would be when I woke up from surgery. When I opened my eyes for the first time, would I be in heaven or still on this earth? Being as truthful as I can be, those raw thoughts were in the front of my mind. I had spent weeks and months preparing for this day while at the same time hearing how difficult and against all odds of success this surgery would be. I had prepared myself for that moment. Rolling down the hall to the surgery room all I could do was look up. The picture of my family was firmly implanted in my mind. But, I had so many wonderful experiences up to this point that if this was the end of my journey, I still could say it was an unmeasurable blessing. Did I have peace in my heart as I was rolled into the cold surgical room? Absolutely!

When the anesthesiologist said count to ten, I was out before I reached the count of five. My body was laying on the bed being prepped for the first incision that would reveal whether it was too bad, and he would give the family that call in the first hour that it did not go well. Or it would reveal the chemo worked, and let's do this. But, my mind was in a gray room with no sound and no recognition of anything going on. There were no thoughts going through my mind. Just total peace.

When we are in the middle of our difficulty, we reach a point where the outcome is going to be revealed very soon. We have fought each day to make it better. We become emotionally and physically worn out. But we also wonder was all the effort worth it? Is it going to be, ok? At that point we have no control at all over what is around the next corner. But, it is also the time when we must let go of any control we were trying to hang on to. It is time to squeeze God's hand and say, "You got this. I am Yours ".

Now the hard part. Are you willing to live with the outcome? When you have asked others to join you in your journey and you have asked God to hold onto your right hand, then that is the time to accept the outcome. You may not think in that moment the outcome is what you wanted, but on the other hand, you must trust God that He knows what the perfect outcome will be for you and your loved ones. It is time to Trust, with a capital "T". When you look back, you will see why the outcome was the right thing for this time in your life.

YOU DON'T ALWAYS need a plan. SOMETIMES you just NEED TO BREATHE, trust, let go and SEE WHAT HAPPENS.

26

Journal Entry December 24, 2022 and January 3, 2023 – Not So Merry Christmas – Mom, Rick and Cathy

December 24, 2022

Me and mom

I hope everyone is having a Merry Christmas. I am feeling better each day, but they are baby steps. However, my 95-year-old mother had a stroke and passed away. My last time seeing mom was at my house when she gave me a big hug and smile. All she wanted was to see me come out of surgery with the cancer removed. She celebrated her first Christmas in Heaven with Dad.

January 3, 2023

Happy New Year to all of my friends and prayer warriors. My journey continues with each day showing baby steps improvement. This has been a very tough going with all that is going on in my life right now. Recovering from major surgery has been very slow. I am constantly tired and weak. I have lost about 35 pounds. As you are aware, my mom had a stroke and passed away a couple days before Christmas. That was another big punch to the gut as well. She was my biggest supporter and everyday called to let me know the cancer was going to disappear. Well, it almost did. The last time I saw mom, she held my hand and gave me a big hug. The funeral was beautiful, and Rick and I got to share some of our favorite memories. Now, we are going through the tedious details of closing mom's accounts and her house.

I met with my oncologist last week and discussed my situation. He was very pleased with the surgery. They removed 1/3 of my pancreas to remove the cancer that remained after the chemo treatments. But, they found cancer in 3 of the 18 lymph node samples they removed. This was good news, but we know the cancer is still there. I will continue with 4 more chemo treatments when I get strong enough. Hopefully in February. He said I am on a curative plan to remove all the cancer, but it is a coin toss if the cancer will return. If it does, we will address each situation as it presents itself. As far as long term outcomes, it varies from worst case 3-5 years to living a normal life. I plan on living several more years and enjoying each living moment.

So, that is the latest. I cannot thank everyone enough for the prayers and support. But I am not out of that rough lava field on the mountain just yet. I see the beautiful ocean below and walk gingerly toward it. Hopefully, it won't take much longer to get there. I hope everyone has a wonderful year 2023!

December 2022 will always be one of the most difficult months I have lived. I had just completed the Whipple surgery in early December with several weeks of pain and healing. Some of those moments I had gone into depression as well. I just wanted to be out of the hospital and home in my own surroundings. But later in the month, around Christmas, I got two other big blows that were as big as cancer. First, on December 22 my mom had a stroke and passed away, and then a couple days after Christmas my wife and I came to an impasse in our marriage, and both decided it was time to go our separate ways. After 18 years, we were calling it quits. I won't go into the details. But, now I was experiencing three of the most difficult and stressful events a person can go through all at the same time. Cancer, loss of a loved one, and divorce. But a very good friend told me, "God will take care of us and not allow us to go through more difficulties in our lives than we can handle". He was still holding my right hand. I guess I needed more challenges to overcome.

Rick and Cathy

Knowing this was coming, God prepared the way for me to better handle these two upcoming life changing events. He spoke to my brother Rick and my sister-in-law about the possibility of moving to Tulsa from Seattle for a short period of time while I was fighting cancer. Rick is a retired Baptist minister, and Cathy is a former schoolteacher and big into missions and ministering to others in need. They also had been around several people that had cancer and were fully aware of the possible negative outcome and difficulties of going through cancer. They asked me what I needed. It was very easy for me to answer that one. I needed them to help mom since she was struggling knowing one of her sons had cancer. She had lost her mother, a sister and brother to cancer. So, she also knew what could happen. But mom was 95 years old and living by herself.

Also, knowing I would be unable to continue my journals for a few weeks, Rick and Cathy stepped in and gave updates to everyone that had been following my progress. It was perfect. I could not have asked for anyone better to step in and help with these items. Obviously, it was unknown to us what was getting ready to happen at the end of December. Their role grew immensely, and they were perfect for the task.

We had Christmas at my house this year a week early since our growing family would be spread in several different cities during Christmas day. We had a great time, and I got a huge hug and grin from mom. One I will forever remember. I was also glad mom got to live long enough to know I had survived the Whipple surgery, and the doctors removed the cancer. This was an answer to prayer for her. But a few days later, mom had a stroke and passed away. Rick called and told me he found mom struggling and called an ambulance. He wanted to know if I wanted to meet them at the hospital. He said mom was unconscious but very peaceful and that I better hurry if I wanted to see her before she passed away. I was in no condition to be going to a hospital, especially when it sounded like she could be gone by the time I got there. It didn't take me long to say no. All I wanted was to remember the last time I saw mom when I got the big hug and loving smile for her son. That was the mom I knew and wanted to remember. As it turned out, she was gone a short time after the call from my brother. Mom would be spending Christmas in heaven with dad. She would be so excited to see him standing there greeting her when she arrived to walk the golden streets of heaven with him.

Mom and Dad

That was just another reason why I believe it was God behind Rick and Cathy moving to Tulsa. A few days later, I gave them the news that my wife and I were getting a divorce. It would be over in the next few weeks. We would be selling the house, and I needed a place to stay. Rick and Cathy did not have a house, so we talked it over and decided to rent mom's home and move in together. After a month of getting ready and having an estate sale, we moved into the place mom loved and shared with dad for over 35 years. She would be so happy to know her sons were living together and especially in her house. Unbeknownst to any of us, I would need to lean on the caring hearts of Rick and Cathy for quite a while longer before I could come and go on my own. I really believe I was their next mission project. They are amazing. As for my kids and grandkids? They were very thankful and excited that I would be moving in with Rick and Cathy. They could already see a positive change in my spirits.

All I can say, is that God is good all the time. All the time God is good. He is watching over me.

Me, Mom and Rick

Rick and I spoke a few words and told a few mom stories at her funeral. It was hard and emotional, but the support was just off the charts. Here is a poem I shared in the service.

"MY FIRST CHRISTMAS IN HEAVEN"

I can see the countless Christmas trees around the world below
With tiny lights like heaven's stars reflecting on the snow.
The sight is so spectacular; please wipe away the tears
For I am spending Christmas with Jesus this year.
I hear the many Christmas songs that people hold so dear
But the sound of music can't compare with the Christmas choir up here.
I have no words to tell you, the joy their faces bring,
For it is beyond description to hear the angels sing.
I know how much you miss me; I see the pain inside your heart
But I am not so far away, we really aren't apart.
So be happy for me, dear one, you know I hold you dear
And be glad I'm spending Christmas with Jesus Christ this year!
I sent you a special gift from my heavenly home above
I sent you each a memory of my undying love.
After all love is a gift, more precious than pure gold
It was always most important in the stories Jesus told.
Please love and keep each other as my Father said to do,
For I can't count the blessings of love He has for each of you.
So have a Merry Christmas, all of you whom I hold dear,
Remember, I am spending Christmas with Jesus Christ this year.

27

Journal Entry February 11, 2023
−Learn From Your Experiences

Before, I give you my latest update, thank you so much for your continued love and support. I have been so humbled and rewarded for your efforts and concerns. Every day I receive encouragement from someone new, and in many cases people I don't know, or haven't heard from or seen in years. You are amazing people. THANK YOU! I am now receiving chemo treatments again after the surgery. I have completed one and have three more to go. I always said I did not want to go through chemo treatments again, but after the difficult "Whipple" surgery and the recovery, I welcome the chemo treatments. My hands and feet are constantly numb and tingling, like neuropathy patients encounter, and my appetite and tastebuds are leaving again. But after nine chemo treatments, I know how to better handle the side effects this go around. It is what it is!

I also want to thank those that attended Mom's funeral and/or reached out to Rick and me. With lots of great memories to share and a few difficult emotional moments for both of us, we made it through the funeral. She would have been so blessed.

Please continue to pray for our "unnamed foxhole friends" who are still fighting their cancer and other illnesses. Many on the list are getting well and getting back to normal lives!! Also, remember Larry Byrd as he continues to fight something new each week. This time, he recently fell on the ice and broke two ribs. Unbelievable. Suzie, it may be time to put Larry in medical timeout and not let him leave the house. Remove all things around him so that he won't trip on them. Get well Larry and stay safe!

As my journey continued, when I came out of the dark and dangerous forest, I came upon the crest of a hill and saw meadows for as far as I could see blanketed in beautiful multicolored flowers. In the valley below, you were getting ready to celebrate your efforts of so many prayers for so many that have been answered. After the celebration, I continued my journey up another mountainside and when I reached the top, I saw a beautiful ocean in the far-off distance. However, to get there, I had to climb down through fields of lava rock left from a volcano eruption many years before.

It was a difficult climb down the mountainside and a slow process, but I was determined to make it. Patience! Right? You are going to come out of this next phase a better person and a blessed person! And I have!!

I have finally reached the bottom of the mountain and am standing on the soft sandy shore. I am looking out across the most beautiful blue green waters of the ocean you have ever seen. I take off my worn-out shoes, and just let the sand and water run across my feet and through my toes. It feels so good. It has been a long journey to reach this point. But a journey I was prepared to make and beat this cancer.

Time for a rest and reflection on where I go from here. I don't see any boats to hitch a ride and nothing but beautiful peaceful shoreline as far as I can see. Now what?

As I stand here, with my hands in my pocket, I am looking at my beautiful surroundings. I am a very blessed person. I look down and see all these little sand crabs being washed into shore with the rolling but gentle waves. Then they scamper back into the ocean. Just to do it again with the next wave. They seem to be having so much fun.

I look out into the ocean for several yards and see a large fin. Is that a shark lurking in the shallow waters? It reminds me that there is always danger and more curve balls waiting to be thrown in life's journey. Are you going to be ready and hit the curve ball or let it slide by for a strike? As for me, I have lots of friends and family that are always there for me. I have God who said give me your right hand and I will take care of you. And I have months of fighting cancer and a difficult journey of experience to lean on when the next curve ball is thrown.

What did I learn? I am just an ordinary guy who got pancreatic cancer. I am nothing special. But I am a fighter and was determined to fight all the way. Even though I had my doubting moments, I was determined to not let the cancer beat me. I had no control over the cancer itself, but I did have control over my spirits. I had friends to lift me up and keep my spirits up. Remember, it takes a team, it takes patience, one step at a time, one inning at a time, one pitch at a time, and if I have one out left in the inning or the game I can still win. I am not done until the last out is made. You don't win in games or life without your team or support structure behind you and encouraging you along the way.

As I look back, it's not the pain, the fear, the surgeries, and the chemo treatments that I remember the most. It is my McLain High School friends that I have not seen or heard from for years that have given me encouragement. It is my college friends that I met that are still giving me some of the best days of my life. It is my TU Baseball fraternity of team-mates and brothers that I have lived through the life lessons of playing a game that has built a bond that can never be broken. It is my brothers and sisters in the TU athletic department and Letterwinners Board that have given me encouragement and an opportunity to give a little service back to those athletes that know what it is like to compete on the athletic field. That is special. It is my golfing, fishing and professional career friends that have been with me for years. It is my Holland Hall family that gave me so many rewarding years. It is my church and spiritual friends that have always been with me and understand the power of prayer and pick me up when I am feeling weak. It is my new friends that I don't even know, that have given me support and encouragement. It is my family that I know I can always count on even when I may not be a fun person to be around. Unconditional love!

These are the things I remember. These are the things that really matter in life. Last week, I was so humbled and blessed when I decided to go visit John Harris Sunday School class in person just to thank them for praying for me every week. What an amazing group of people. I felt like I already knew them. The experiences continue.

So, the cancer is still being treated. It can come back at any point in time. There is the unknown always out there. But that is life. We all face the unknown. Are we going to live in fear of the unknown? Let it drag us down? Let life's curve balls strike us out?

I am staring at the ocean as I reflect on my past. Then, I see another fin sticking out of the water. Man, the sharks must have found a great area to feed on. Then, I see a couple roll over in the water, and I can see their backs more clearly.

Those aren't sharks. That is several dolphins feeding and playing in the shallows of the water. They seem to really enjoy playing with each other and frolicking in the beautiful waters. They know there is always danger out there, but that is not going to deter them from living and enjoying each other. If danger threatens one of them, they will all join to become a mighty force in the battle. I even notice as they swim by, I can see a glance my way. Wow! They seem to be so happy.

So, where do I go from here? What is around the next corner? I have no idea! But, I am not going to live in fear of the cancer coming back or another curve ball being thrown my way. I am going to be blessed I have lived this journey. I am going to be a better person. I am going to give back any way I can because I have experienced the results of others giving to me.

I am going to be Happy and love life, whatever I have left. I am going to be a Dolphin!

Thank you and I love you....Whit

When we go through difficult periods in our lives, we must remember these are the times when we learn and prepare us for the next obstacle. Remember what you have been through. The pain, the heartbreak and maybe the loss of a loved one. How did you get through those difficult times? Did you do it by yourself? I would venture to say you had lots of support and most likely that one true friend you could trust or just talk to.

In my case, the journey was a long journey of several months. Yours may be only a few days or possibly weeks and months as well. Look back on your journey and what you learned. You will most likely have another situation where you will have to use the lessons you learned. However, possibly the next time you may be the person that is supporting someone else. Now you can relate to their difficulties and speak to them from experience.

As you can tell from my journals and the analogies I used, I needed frequent pauses and times to rest and reflect. I always knew there could be another curve ball or situation that I will be facing in the future. So, take that pause and reflect and file those learning experiences away in your mind so you can call upon those whenever you need them. If you reflect inward, you will also realize you are a stronger person as well. The unknowns will not be your enemy to fear, but just another challenge that you are prepared to face head-on.

But most of all, trust in yourself and your faith. You already know God will hold your right hand and lead you through those challenging moments. Let hope in each situation, and know that the bright light of hope is just waiting to shine through those dark clouds.

28

Journal Entry March 11, 2023 – Cherish the Moments

It has been a few weeks since I gave an update, so here we go.

Thank you for your continued support. You probably didn't think you would have to keep doing this so long. Yes, it has been a long and difficult journey that I could only make with your amazing support. Don't forget Larry Byrd, Brian Humphrey, and all our unnamed foxhole friends! They continue to be blessed and strengthened by your support as well.

I have completed 3 rounds (11 total) of chemo this phase and have one more next Wednesday, March 15. After this, I will have another CT scan to see how it worked. Anxious? Not really. It is what it is. I am prepared for whatever is presented to me. From a selfish standpoint, I hope this long journey hasn't been for naught, and I have bought a few more years. However, what am I saying? I have always said I am blessed to have traveled this journey and how much I have learned. If the journey ends soon, then it has been worth it anyway. So, scratch that momentary chemo brain doubt I mentioned a couple moments ago. Wow, you have blessed me, and I feel it every day.

So, I am still meandering on the beach with the beautiful blue green waters rolling into the shore and across my bare toes. The Dolphins continue to show up every few days and give me a wonderful show of love while playing with their pod family. It really lifts my spirits. They are probably thinking, why is he still here and why hasn't he figured out the next phase of his journey?

You know, that is a great question. Let me try to explain it from my perspective of an unknown future. I guess, technically, we all think we have our lives all planned out and that is the way it is going to be. I have been wandering along the beach for several days. Not really spending so much time thinking but resting and just going with the flow of the day. Sometimes it rains, sometimes it is windy bringing in high waves from the ocean, but most days it is a beautiful sunny day. The other day I was watching the horizon get darker and darker. Then, flashes of lightning steak across the sky. It was coming my way. It was another curveball I had to face. Now what? Really? I have traveled so far on my journey with cancer, then losing mom along the way and now this? I will prevail with the support and love I get each day.

So, here I sat on a piece of driftwood that had drifted upon the shore and found a perfect resting place under a shady tree. It is just the right height to make a chair. It was beckoning me to come and sit down. So, I did.

I am sitting here reflecting on the past, but also, I need to move forward. But where? Doing what? I lived through a lot during my journey. I have learned a lot about myself. I have learned a lot from my friends,

*my family, and people I never knew and may never meet. I look down
at my feet watching the water and sand trickling between my toes. Then,
I realize each of those individual nuggets of sand represents the people I
have supporting me. I rub my hands along the sides of the driftwood I am
sitting on and marvel how smooth it is. Then I realized that represents the
changes in me because of my journey. I begin to see why I have always said
I am blessed to have this journey and will forever be thankful. The stormy
days and the sunny days!*

*I think about life before my
journey with cancer. I had a good
and normal life. But not great.
So many wonderful memories and
some not so good. Each of those
memories were moments in time.
As athletes, we often remember the big base hit, the key basket made, the
big hit that caused a fumble. Those we cherish. But, often we also remember the strikeout, the missed shot, or the missed tackle, and sometimes those
memories overtake the good memories. But, with each of those moments in
time, do you remember the final score? Who won the game?*

*How often do we look ahead and think we have our lives planned out
and then later it doesn't turn out how we had it planned. Or, we spend
so much time planning the future and worrying about the future that
it takes away the moments we live in now. It is the moments that are
important. It is the moment we get immediate feedback. It is the moments
that form our future. It is the moments that form us.*

*So, back to my driftwood on which I am sitting. This piece of driftwood
used to be part of a large tree, with rough bark and branches extending out
to form the tree. But, something unplanned happened to the tree and this
branch. It ended up in the ocean all rough and broken. But, day after day*

it was battered around by the waves. The rough bark and branches were broken off and what was left was made smooth to the touch. That broken tree became a favorite resting place. It had a new purpose in helping me look and move forward.

Those nuggets of sand? They wash upon the shore and often drift back into the water waiting for another wave to bring them back again. But they are always there giving structure and support to the piece of driftwood and comfort to my feet as they trickle between my toes. I can always count on them to give my feet a nice massage. It feels so good.

My journey has made me a new person, but a journey that will always continue and continue to transform me for the better. It has given me so much joy and so many memorable moments. I no longer make my future a priority. Sure, I look ahead, but I no longer worry about something that may or may not happen. Cherish the moments.

I have always had great friends and a great family. Friends I knew and some that I knew very well. Family I would do anything for unconditionally. But did I really know them? My journey has enriched my fondness and love for them that is more meaningful and rewarding than I could possibly realize or understand.

So, I often found I was looking to the days after cancer that I would do the things I have dreamed. The days I could start living and enjoying life again. Be happy again. But, I realized, I am living the future every day. Every moment. My life is not on hold while I wait for the outcome of the cancer. I am not going to roam and meander the beautiful shores of this beach any longer. I have so many moments to live and explore. Moments to share with my family and my friends. Each day I sit here on the driftwood trying to figure out my future, I have wasted another moment I could be living and sharing.

So, there are some amazing opportunities waiting for me to just take the next step forward. There are beautiful meadows and mountains for me to climb just around the corner. It is time for me to go.

With sadness and joy, I must bid goodbye to my dolphin friends, my nuggets of sand and my driftwood sanctuary. There is a big, beautiful world full of my family, friends and so many new friends I hope to meet waiting for me.

Remember, it is the moments in our lives that are important. Not the planning and worrying of some future that may or not happen. Your continued support and love are the moments I can feel right now....Have a wonderful day. Have a great moment and cherish it.

Love you, Whit

So often in life, we spend more time planning and sometimes worrying about the future that we forget about what is going on today in our lives. How many times have you said, "When I retire, I am going to do this, and I am going to do that." But life doesn't

work that way unfortunately. Yes, we need to plan and ensure we are financially able to support our lifestyle when we retire. It is great to dream of traveling or living in that lake house or spending time with the grandkids. But, what if you develop cancer or encounter another difficulty in your life that derails all those plans you have been dreaming about? If the happiness in your life is based upon what you have planned, then you are likely to fail your expectations. So, plan for those days, but don't let your happiness in life be conditional upon the life that you have planned. You might realize you found something that is better than you planned.

I bought an Audi TT two seat roadster the first year they came out. It was a great car and lots of fun. Over time it was going to be a classic car. I took care of it and planned for all those beautiful days of retirement just driving around with the top down. There would be no worries in life. Just enjoying the openness of a convertible zipping around the countryside. I had it all planned out. What a life it was going to be. But, as I was reaching retirement, I started having grandkids pop up in my life. I loved my grandkids and wanted to share so many wonderful moments with them. All I had was my Audi TT since I didn't need another car. But, there was no room in the Audi for me to take the grandkids anywhere. I quickly realized that those plans for my happiness in retirement were going to have to change. So, I sold my Audi TT roadster for a truck and a boat. Now, I have lots of room for the grandkids and we can go to the lake to fish, swim, or just enjoy the openness of the air, but on the lake. This opened better opportunities for happy moments than what I had planned. So, you never know what the future holds.

Whatever you enjoy doing and who you do them with, cherish those moments.

29

Journal Entry April 13, 2023 – I Am Not a Statistic

My latest update....When I left the beautiful beach, I started climbing the mountain that rose about 2000 feet above the ocean. I found a rudimentary path going up the mountain to where I had no clue. It wasn't a human path, but probably a path carved out by the animals roaming these mountains. I had seen mountain goats in the far-off distance occasionally. I also saw what I thought was a mountain lion as well. But, they all stayed clear of this human that was roaming the beach. This human they saw was frail looking and wandering back and forth on the beach. Sometimes, it looked like he was talking to the ocean and the dolphins that would swim by and give him a look as well. Then, other times he was sitting on an old piece of driftwood that had washed up onto the shore. Just sitting there looking off into the distance in a blank stare. He seemed lost and not sure where to go. But in a strange way, he looked peaceful and ready for whatever the next day brought. Kind of like he was treating each moment as something to cherish and not worried about the future. Well, they were right in what they saw. Being confused is not the right word, but being contemplative about an unknown future would better describe it.

As I finally reached the top of the mountain, I saw a fork in the road. One leading down into what looked like a dense forest. One like the one I had traveled on several weeks ago. Then, the other path looked like beautiful meadows and full of flowers. Much like the meadows, I crossed climbing the mountain that would take me down to the ocean beach. I smile when I think of Yogi Berra, the great New York Yankee Hall of Fame catcher. He always said, if you come to a fork in the road....take it. Well, I am at that fork in the road. However, which path should I take? It seems an easy choice of beautiful meadows instead of the dark dense forest.

So, I sit on the ground contemplating which way to go. The path that seems the easiest or the one that looks more difficult. I remember my journey up these mountains. I traveled through a dark dense forest. It was treacherous and very difficult at times. But, those days tested me and made me a better person through those trials. Then, I came upon the beautiful valley and the lush meadows of multicolored flowers that blanketed the floor of the valley. It was kind of like a brief pause after the difficult journey. A moment in the journey that said, you have come this far, so relax for a while. The journey is not over.

So, as I am sitting here trying to decide what path to take, I lay on my back and just stare at the big fluffy clouds slowly moving across the vast blue sky. I look back on my journey again and all the love, prayers and support that gave me strength

to make it this far. I remember the first morning after finding out I had pancreatic cancer, and God said, "give me your right hand and I will take care of you." I have never let go. Sometimes I had to hold on tighter, to face a difficult period.

Recently, I was having a tough day and called the cancer clinic. They told me to rush back to the clinic. So, I did. I was confronted with those rooms and all those chairs where we got our chemo treatments. I remembered leaving there after my last chemo treatment with a tear in my eye and a lump in my throat. Thinking I would not be back. But, here I was back again. Being treated for dehydration by those amazing nurses once again. They did not know what caused the nausea and constant throwing up, but they did know they needed to fill me up with fluids quickly. What amazing nurses they are to care for the people that in several cases their lives are placed in their hands.

Then, I think of my brother Rick and my sister-in-law, Cathy rushing me to the clinic that day after living through the mess I was in that morning. Their love and compassion are fabulous. Since we moved into mom's house together, I have constant love and positive feelings everyday coming from them. It's like when the morning sun starts to rise in the east, you know it is going to be a good day. I cannot tell them how much they mean to me. I can't find the right words. But, they are very special people.

I have been blessed by so many wonderful friends and family, that I know I will have all the support during my unknown future. Each of my kids and my close friends are always there for me and always wanting to know what they can do for me. I am so beholden to them. God is my rock and foundation. But, my friends are part of that foundation.

Recently, I decided to give a round of golf a try. The game was terrible but being able to finish 18 holes was encouraging. Just going out with Roger Adams, Ken Knight, and my brother was so uplifting. Then, I had a CT scan this past week. I will meet with the oncologist next week to go over the results. However, my daughter, Cathleen, went onto my portal and saw the results. Based upon her unprofessional medical interpretations of the report, she called me early in the morning to tell me..."Dad, the report says there is no sign of cancer!" Man, that was great news. But with cautious optimism, I gladly accept the results. Again, your prayers and support for me have been heard and answered by God and felt again. Thank you!

So, what about the future? We have no idea what our future holds. None of us. Especially those with cancer or other illnesses that could take your life. I have read the internet and all kinds of medical journals about my type of cancer. The odds are not in my favor, and it will likely return. It can be discouraging and break your will if you let yourself believe all the stuff on the internet. But Cathleen told me several weeks ago...."Dad, you are not a statistic." What an encouraging way to look at it. It really changed my mood and outlook. I AM NOT A STATISTIC! I can beat this. Like I said in a previous update, live for the moments in life. Cherish and enjoy them. We are all going to die someday anyway. Live and love life. There is so much good around us.

The other part of this equation, "Let Hope In". My pastor, David Emery, spoke about this last Sunday. I swear he is always talking to me. LET HOPE IN.......think about that. Sometimes we feel dejected and rejected by the world around us. But what is life without Hope? I remember my mom, before she passed away, always praying that after the chemo treatments before the Whipple surgery, the cancer would be gone, and they wouldn't have to perform surgery. I always tried to dampen her expectations and prayer by telling her, the doctors said the cancer will still be there and we will have to do surgery. But she thrived on that Hope. She was so pleased when the chemo killed more of the cancer than the doctors expected. We still had surgery, but her Hope kept her encouraged.

Another example. You all know Brian Humphrey gives me inspiration every time I visit him. The prognosis of him recovering from his stroke and paralysis on the right side is that it will never heal or get better. But each time I visit Brian, he proudly shows me how he can move his right leg. Each time is greater than the last time. I don't know if he will ever gain the use of his leg or not, but he lives on Hope. I am now allowing in my mind and heart to....LET HOPE IN. If he could get the use of his right leg, well that would be a game changer.

When Roger Adams and I visited Brian last week, he was so excited and giving us fist bumps because he was moving his right foot. Whatever your thoughts on his recovery, who are we to take away his hope or even better, not believe in Hope as well. Hope gives us encouragement, which gives us positive power, which gives us a reason to continue our fight. Believe in Hope and Let it In.

Remember that baseball game we played against Arizona State after being down 10-3 in the last inning? And we came back and won 11-10? I told you about this several updates ago. If we did not have hope or believed in the statistics that you can't win games down this many runs, then why play the game. Just give up. But instead stay hopeful and don't believe you are a statistic. Then you have a great chance of winning the game and fighting as long as you still have one out left.

So, as I stare at the clouds and think about where I am headed next, I can say for certain, "God will be holding my right hand; I have an amazing army of friends and family walking beside me; I will Let Hope In and I am not a statistic!"

I love you....Whit

I will still be on my journey for quite a while longer getting CT scans every three to four months for the next five years. The odds of cancer returning are very possible the first two years. Then the odds turn in my favor of cancer not returning. I have learned a lot on this journey. One of those lessons was to be patient. Take it one step at a time. I am not one to sit around and lament my situation for the next five years. I am going to live for each moment every day. I am going to cherish those moments I can spend time with my kids and grandkids. I know how I got this far in my journey, and it was always having hope I would get better. Your attitude is a powerful thing in controlling how you will live. A positive attitude is also very powerful in helping the healing process.

As I read about my cancer and the odds of cancer returning it can be depressing. But, the advice I received from Cathleen really hit home. "Dad, you are not a statistic." Just those words changed my attitude. Those odds are just numbers. Someone must beat the odds, why not me? I can do this. I will not live the rest of my life in fear and worrying about the cancer returning.

As you face your difficulties, don't let the odds beat you down and depress you. Keep pressing forward and just say "I am not a statistic".

30

Journal Entry June 13, 2023 –
Reach for the Stars

Hi guys,

It has been a while since I posted an update. Mostly because things don't change as frequently as they did during the chemo phases. Until I ring the bell at the cancer institute signifying I am cancer free, my journey will continue. Currently I am still in the phase with higher rates of cancer returning. But, I did want to give an update and also shed light on a few experiences that might be helpful for those on similar journeys. So here goes....

It has been a few weeks since my last scan that showed the cancer was gone. Of course, this was only the first scan of many to come to keep an eye on my condition. I am still in the unfavorable condition that the cancer will most likely return. After year two, the odds will turn in my favor. I still have side effects from the cancer surgery and the chemo treatments. I still fight stomach issues each day and still have severe neuropathy. I take about 15 pills every day. But I am learning how to adjust to these remaining conditions. "It is what it is" and "life goes on." It could be a lot worse, so I am not complaining.

My life now is transitioning from a life of fighting cancer for 18 months and any future plans were not in the picture. Now, I am beginning to see the future and making plans for a longer life. It could be 1 to 2 years up to a normal life. At my age, 75, I guess you could say I am already deep into the normal life span and probably on borrowed time anyway. I will take any extra days, months, and years I am given. My appetite and taste buds have returned. My energy level and weight are gradually getting better. I am doing everything I want and desire to do. Maybe not as fast.

I am learning everyday how to live my life going forward. What does that look like? I have watched Suzi and Larry Byrd and John Klahr as they progress throughout their lives after cancer. As always, I am inspired by how each of them continues their journeys.

My mind is my biggest foe now. I am living with my brother Rick and sister-in-law, Cathy, in mom's former home in Owasso. It is going well. They recently took me with them for a week to Cabo to take my mind off the last several months. That was a great trip that got me jumped started in getting this next phase of my life moving forward. With my existing lingering health issues, I often feel like a burden to them. So, I have got to get this figured out. But, they have been so patient and helpful to me.

From our balcony in Los Cabo

One thing I feel the most is the urge to do all the things I have on my bucket list. However, my bucket list is growing instead of being checked off. Yes, I still have sky diving near the top of the list. I want to do things with my family; I want to do things with my friends; I want to be used to help someone who may have to travel a journey like mine; I want to pass it forward all the amazing things and support people have given to me as I have traveled my journey. It has changed my life, and I am blessed to take this journey. You have given me an infinity of blessings.

When I last updated my journey, I had reached the summit of a mountain high above the ocean below. There was a path that seemed to lead to beautiful meadows blanketed with flowers. There was another path leading into the dense and dark forest. Much like the one I traveled before. As I laid back my head on the ground and looked up at the blue sky with big puffy white clouds, I was trying to find my way forward. What will my life be like now? What is it supposed to look like? How much longer do I have to live? What can I do to make a difference in someone's life? How can I pass it forward? What am I passing forward anyway? Oh, there it is....the big question. What am I passing forward? Why did I go through 18 months fighting cancer that has a very low survival rate. Why am I not a statistic, as my daughter Cathleen challenged me to not become a statistic. Why did I experience such an amazing journey filled with blessings along each step? Why did God tell me on the first morning after I found out I had cancer to hold out my right hand and he would hold my hand and take care of me? Why me? I am just an ordinary guy with lots of friends. More than I could ever realize if not for this journey.

Oh....another thought....what are each of us doing with our lives and what are we passing forward? Is it to teach our kids and grandkids how to live and enjoy life? Is it to leave something positive in someone's life? This question and trying to answer it is way above my pay grade. I am still trying to figure out my life. So, I will leave it for you to figure it out in your own lives.

I do know from my experiences growing up, playing baseball at TU, being on the competitive field or just going through tough times, the winners learn from those experiences and dust themselves off and get back in the fight to win. Losers just sit there and feel sorry for themselves and wonder why me? I can say firsthand all of you reading these words have risen to the occasion and left a huge mark in my life. I have fought beside most of you on the playing field and many in life situations. You dusted yourself off and took on the challenge. You are a winner. I thank you for "having my back".

Well, as I mentioned before, I saw what I thought were mountain goats high up on the sides of a massive mountain. As I rolled over onto my side, I put my head on my propped-up arm and just watched them climb higher and higher. Climbing over and around huge boulders that had life threatening consequences with one wrong step. But, they climbed without fear. They didn't worry about the next step, the next day or the next year. They were climbing and living life. Higher and higher they went. Just like they were trying to reach the stars.

As I was leaning on my elbow, watching these amazing mountain goats, I started paying attention to what I thought was thunder in the background. So, I better get up and decide which path and where I was going. I better find cover. Then I looked around and the sky was a beautiful blue sky with those big puffy white clouds streaming by. I don't see a storm on the horizon. It sounded like it was coming from somewhere below me. How can that be? What is it? I continued to walk along the summit of the mountain until I could see the ocean below. Then I witnessed the most amazing thing I have seen from the ocean. As I just sat there in amazement, I was watching waves of the ocean forming a mile off the shore and as they continued to roll toward the shore, they would get larger and larger. As they neared the shore, their own weight of forming a beautiful rolling wave would become so large it curled under and crashed into the shore with a huge thunderous clap, and the wave would turn into a huge white foam climbing over 20 feet into the air. Not only was it amazing, but it was also beautiful as I sat there in awe watching it rollback into the ocean to become another loud thunderous wave. There was no wind, just a long stillness of the ocean making quiet waves until it made a thunderous thing of beauty.

As I watch, I am reminded what else God told me later in my journey. He said "When ongoing problems require you to stick it out over the long haul, beware of responding by grimly gritting your teeth...just passing the time in a gloomy frame of mind. This passive, negative attitude is not the way I want you to approach difficulties. Actually, the more difficult your circumstance, the more you gain from it." God's power is/was so great it turned my journey into Joy.

So, I got the message and I saw the wonder still out there to witness and share. There are more memories to make; there are more moments to share; and there are more opportunities to pass forward the experiences of a journey I will forever be blessed I lived. There is so much more to live.

I am going to take another path that was hidden this whole time. One that was less traveled than the other two. This path leads up to the massive rock covered mountain. I am going to follow those mountain goats with the same determination without fear of falling or what tomorrow brings. I have decided I am going to climb higher and higher and "reach for the stars." I hope we can share them together. All you must do is look up!

Thank you for all your support and for our "unnamed friends" as well. You are my "foxhole friends"!...I love you....Whit

After spending several days and weeks on the beach trying to recover and get my thoughts together, I decided it was time to start living for the future rather than just getting by each day one step at a time. It was time to move on and start climbing back to the top of the mountain and decide where I would go from here. My mind was still trying to comprehend everything I had learned on this journey. Knowing I still had a few more years of uncertainty ahead of me, it was not the time to stop living and wait five years before I get the green light the cancer is gone.

As I reached the top of the mountain, I could see forever. Meadows in one direction and higher mountains the other direction. Above me were beautiful blue skies with big white puffy clouds. They were just slowly moving and seemed to be sitting there above me. As I lay on my side with my chin resting on my hand and elbow propping me up, I started contemplating my next path. I could either take the path to the meadows or the other path to the dark forest. But, there was one other path I could take that was hidden in the brush. It was heading up toward the direction where I could barely see mountain goats on the cliffs. It looked like they were in the clouds, and so close to the stars that came out at nightfall. It was if they were climbing higher and higher so they could stand among the stars. They were fearless as they walked along the ragged boulders.

When we have been through our difficult moments and finally come out of the dark clouds we seemed to have lived in, we finally see the sun shining bright again. Is our journey over? Probably not, but the worst part is behind you. You have learned a lot about yourself and learned so many lessons. Now you are ready to move on and use what you have learned. You now have the confidence you made it and are stronger person from the experience. Hopefully you realize you did not travel the path alone, but you had God and others holding your hand as you faced each twist and turn of the journey.

So, I have laid here long enough. I have watched the clouds moving by and made my decision which path to take.

It will be dark soon, so I must move on. Which path am I going to take? The dark forest, the beautiful mountain meadows or the hidden path leading upward?

As I was laying in the meadow, I remember something God told me while on my journey. He said...."When ongoing problems require you to stick it out over the long haul, beware of responding by grimly gritting your teeth...just passing the time in a gloomy frame of mind. This passive, negative attitude is not the way I want you to approach difficulties. Actually, the more difficult your circumstance, the more you gain from it."

Reach for the Stars

I have decided I have gained a lot from my difficult journey. I am not done. God still has more for me to do. I am ready for any obstacle that may get in my way. I am not going to live my life in a passive and gloomy frame of mind. I am going to take the hidden path that leads to the top of the mountain. I am going to follow the goats, and I am going to "reach for the stars."

31

Journal Entry December 8, 2023
- One Year Later

Today, December 8th, is a very special day for me and my family. I am sure you have special days as well. If you don't, think for a bit and try to remember a day that changed your life or someone in your family. Was it just another day? Or was it a day to remember? Was it one of those special moments we talk about or was it a day of sadness we want to forget? Has that day changed your life? A day that made you a better person or a day that made you thankful for what you have?

Sometimes it's the little things that can have such big impacts on our lives. Now, you may not realize what just happened and how it shifted your life. The realization of that moment may not come until later.

My special moment that changed my life was a simple smile and words, "I love you. I will see you soon".

Today, one year later, my kids, Ryan, Barbe and Cathleen, reminded me today, December 8th was an anniversary and a day of celebration. I thought for a moment and couldn't remember. They said this was the day you had your Whipple surgery, and they removed the cancer from your pancreas. Then those moments of a year ago came rushing back to the front of my mind. Inside my head, I became fearful but at peace. Tears were building from that memory and what the day could have held.

You see, I knew I wasn't supposed to survive the surgery, but I never told my kids. They also knew I wasn't supposed to survive the surgery, but they did not want to tell their Dad. As I was lying on the bed and the nurse was ready to take me to the operating room, she paused for a moment, as if she knew also, so that I could look at my kids and they in turn could look at me. With forced smiles, like it was going to be ok, we uttered the simple words, "I love you and will see you in a few hours". As I was wheeled to the operating room and they walked to the waiting room, we all thought that was the last special moment we would share. That was it! No more special moments. But, because of so many people praying and supporting me, God heard the prayers and decided this isn't the end. He will be a changed man. He will experience and be thankful for all the caring support coming from his friends. He will be remember and be thankful for those special moments he has shared.

So today, December 8th, 2023, one year later, I am sharing an anniversary with my kids because of you asking God to place his healing hand on my body. When it all started, God said give me your right hand and I will take care of you. And he did!

Thank you for everything you have done for me and my family. I am a very blessed man. Have a wonderful Christmas, and don't forget to look for those little special moments you will most likely have this Christmas. Remember it might be one of those moments that could change your life.

Love you all, and Merry Christmas...............................Whit

I had traveled a long and difficult journey. I could not wait to get to the Whipple surgery because it was my only hope of beating the cancer living on my pancreas. But, I also knew the odds were very much against my survival of the surgery. My doctors were great at explaining to me each step of the surgery and how complex and serious this was. The Whipple surgery is one of the top two most complex and difficult surgeries a person can undergo.

I knew God had my hand, and kept me at peace during my journey. Somehow, I was at peace going through the surgery. It was my only chance. But, I also knew I was in a win-win situation. I would either have more days on earth with my family and friends or I would be going to heaven and joining my family and friends that were already there. But I really did not want to leave my family. Not now. But, I had to place my trust in God that He knew what was best.

As I was lying on the bed to take me to the operating room, I thought this was it. I wasn't going to survive the surgery. This was the last time I would see my kids. But, I could not bring it upon myself to tell them this was our "goodbye" moment. Later, the kids told me they felt the same way, but could not tell me how they felt.

So, we looked each other in the eye for what each of us thought was the final moment and forced a smile and said "I love you and will see you in a few hours". But as I was wheeled to the operating room tears rushed to my eyes, but my mind was swirling around with quick memories of past years. Once I was wheeled into the operating room everyone was waiting for me. The doctors and nurses were there giving me encouragement and preparing me for the surgery. Then I received my anesthesia and within a few seconds my world went blank. Where would I be when I wake up?

When we are nearing the end of our journey, or the obstacles are being cleared away, we are faced with the results. How did we do? Will we accept the results? What do I do next? Many questions will have been answered and a new direction will be revealed.

If you traveled your journey trusting God, then no matter the ending, you will know it is God's will, and the best possible ending for this situation. It is also a new beginning that's even better.

You will also find you are a changed person and a better person for living your difficulty. Embrace this new person you have become and live a thankful life. But most of all, remember it was God holding your hand that allowed you to survive a difficult time. One that you can now learn from and be better prepared for when that next obstacle gets in your way. Give God the praise and always call upon Him. Even just to talk to Him, and just say thank you for being in my life. If you haven't had that moment with God, now is a great time to ask Him to show you how He can always be in your heart and mind. He is ready, are you?

32

Journal Entry December 18, 2023 - My Changing World

Merry Christmas to everyone. You didn't think you could get away without me sharing another story, did you? Not a chance!

Well, the last time I left you, I had decided to climb the steep cliffs of the mountains and join the mountain goats that wandered fearlessly roaming along the huge boulders at the top of the mountain. Of course, they had no fear jumping from one boulder to another, but as for me, I bear hug each boulder trying to reach those stars in the heavens. I often lay on my back each evening watching a spectacular light show with amazing colors you don't see on earth. The shooting star display is just amazing. Every night it is a different show of splendid beauty.

During the daylight hours, I have another view that will leave you speechless. Just the majesty of it all leaves you speechless. The breath of what you can see in all directions reminds you of days in my

past. Some wonderful days, and others not so wonderful. I can see in the distance the various changes in the landscape. Several miles to my right, is the life before cancer with a path leading to months of chemotherapy and the Whipple surgery. Many miles before me are the dark forest with a difficult path winding among the forest and steep cliffs dropping off to a mountain stream in the valley. Several feet below me in the valley are the beautiful meadows of flowers of all colors. There is the pond with the moose enjoying another meal and the beaver dams holding the water from the stream to create the magnificent pool of water and grow lily pads. Many miles to my left are the ocean where I wandered several days talking to the dolphins and trying to figure out where I would go next. I can barely see the driftwood that spent several days being tossed around in the ocean until its branches became smooth and transformed into a beachside chair. I spent many days sitting on my driftwood chair contemplating the future.

How a person can live through so much in just a few months' time is staggering. I have gone from the Christmas of 2022, when I was undergoing a surgery that I was not supposed to survive, to a Christmas of 2023 with so much joy, and a promise of many years left to live. Yes, I miss my mom, who passed away last Christmas. I remember a marriage that failed in December as well. Now I am living as a single man with my brother and sister-in-law. I cannot express how important Rick and Cathy have been in my life. They have been there every step of the way without one word of regret or showing any signs of "what have we got ourselves into?" Recently, they had to comfort me when I had frequent bouts of unexpected circumstances and two separate hospital stays. But, as I always say, "It is what it is"!

I have I traveled many months of twists and turns, good days, and bad days. Now, I am reflecting on how much my little world has changed. Because of my circumstances, my world is so much larger. That is totally due to the numbers of people that have prayed for and supported me these last several months. I will never forget when my brother told me, Roger, *you don't have just friends, "you have foxhole friends." Amazing what that word represents to each of us. We started off the "TU 1969 Baseball Team" Facebook page for a hangout for all of us former teammates. Now it is a gathering place for a few hundred people to come hangout with us. A place to offer support for one of their "foxhole friends". Yes, we are all brothers and sisters now. Circumstances in life bring friends together. My world and yes, your world is much bigger now than it was a year ago. How great is that!*

My message to each of you, from the bottom of my heart, be thankful for what you have. Be thankful for the world you live in. Be it as small as your close family or as large and as far as you can see from a mountain top. Be thankful. This year you made a difference in my life. I am eternally grateful for each one of you. Remember our "unnamed friends" who wanted to be anonymous with their illness, but wanted your support? Many of them are healed now and I know they are grateful as well for your prayers and support.

So, in closing, as you spend time with your families and friends this Christmas, remember the true meaning of Christmas. Think of that little baby laying in that little bed of straw and how he changed the world. You changed my world this year, go and change the world for someone else this year. How can you do that? Your love and support did that for me. You have an abundance of love and support that you can share again, over, and over. Remember, we are a huge world of "foxhole friends" who will always need our brother and sister to "have our backs someday".

Here is one little example of someone I did not know spreading joy to a stranger. This is not unique, but it was to me being on the receiving end. Several months ago, I pulled into McDonalds to order some food. When I went up to pay, they said the car in front of me had already paid for my meal. Total strangers, just passing forward a little joy. I tried to hurry and catch them so I could thank them, but they were already gone. Unique no, but a joyful moment? Absolutely! You know what, the next day, I did the same thing to the car behind me. Did I look to see how many were in the car first before I decided to pass it forward and pay for their morning breakfast.? Yes, I did, because I was hoping it would be a mom and all the kids in the car. As I drove away, I glanced in the rearview mirror and saw the expressions of shock and joy of what had just happened. Their eyes lit up and the laughter was contagious. As for me? I got a huge inside smile that turned into an outward expression of laughter. It was a simple deed, but one that we both shared together. Total strangers. We never met.

This little story was not about the good deed I received from someone that I decided to pass forward. It was a good deed how I could expand my world to invite someone else in and share a little moment together. It doesn't take much to expand your world of happiness and doing a good deed. Your prayers and support for a brother or sister, a hug for a grand-child or spouse, a smile to a stranger or buying a stranger a meal.

Mary and Joseph delivered a little baby that changed the world! That little baby taught us how to love. Well, that little baby, Jesus, is the reason we have love and can share it with such wonderful friends and loved ones. People I will cherish forever. Even those that I have never met. Thank you!

Baby Jesus was born in the lowest of places among the animals, and became the savior of this world. He told me, "hold my right hand and I will take care of you." I am a very blessed man to have walked this road with Jesus holding my hand throughout my difficult times. He says he will do the same for you if only you ask him.

Looking back over the past year and everything that has happened in my life is just too much to comprehend. I went from a person that had a happy life, to a person that got pancreatic cancer. I have cancer that most people do not survive. Yet here I am a year later, still alive. I lost my mom a few days after the Whipple surgery. She was so happy I had survived. Then a few days after Christmas, my wife and I decided our marriage was not in a good place and decided to end it. I never saw this coming. So, I had a huge Whipple surgery, the loss of my mom and the ending of an 18-year marriage. That seemed a lot to go through at once. But God was still holding my hand. He knew I needed His strength to get me through each of these trials and obstacles that were in my path to recovery. But, He has said He will not give us more challenges than we can handle. I never lost faith in God. As a matter of fact, I grew closer to Him through these tragedies. I needed His help.

Through my journey, I look back at all my wonderful friends and family. They wanted to join me on the journey. They wanted the good news along with the bad news. They wanted to travel the twists and turns of the treacherous paths I had to travel. They knew I needed them now more than ever. Because of this journey, their faith grew as well, and they supported me with their support and prayers. Then the word spread about my journal entries and my journey. More and more people wanted to support me and follow my journey.

My world grew to a much larger world than I will ever know. But what mattered was God heard their prayers and saw the growing numbers supporting me. He answered their prayers and took care of me, just like He said when He grabbed my hand.

Like I have always said at the beginning of my journey, "I know I am living the journey, but I don't want the journey to be about me, I want it to be what happened during the journey. I want people to know that God's power through His people praying, can change someone's world. My world is so much bigger now and I am a very blessed man."

33

I Dream to Ring the Bell

Before I give an update on my current situation, I am dedicating my book to a few people that made my journey a success. Without these people, the journey would not have been possible.

I have mentioned several times my oncologist, Dr. Scott Cole, and his staff and my Whipple surgeon and his staff, Dr. Edward Cho. Not only are their skills top class, but they have always explained each step in a language I could understand. They have always given me all the time I needed to answer any of my questions and most importantly speak honestly with me. I trust them with my life, and I could not be in better hands.

To all the people that work at the Oklahoma Cancer Specialists and Research Institute, and especially the nurses who operate the 100 plus beds of cancer patients giving them their chemotherapy cocktails. I was in those chairs countless hours, and I never experienced one negative moment from any of them. With the number of patients and the high stress level they work under, not one time did anyone have a bad day. It was always about taking care of their cancer patients and trying to save our lives. They did it with compassion for each one of us and always in a manner that made us comfortable and glad to be in their care. We each had a name and an illness, but never just another number sitting in a numbered cubicle. We were real people with serious issues and treated that way.

Kayla Malay was one of those beautiful people that work at OCSRI. Thank you, Kayla.

During my journey, I was humbled by the people that were fighting cancer and other serious illnesses that trusted me with their conditions but wanted to be left unnamed. These were our "unnamed foxhole friends" that everyone supported and prayed for them just as they supported me. Several have recovered from their illnesses, but a few others are still on their journeys. They inspired me.

The reason I made it this far in my journey was all the people that offered up their prayers and support. I truly believe, if it wasn't for the number of people supporting me and asking God to heal me, I would have had a different ending. God heard the requests from so many friends, churches, and people I did not know, that He said, "I hear you and will grant your request". Thank you, my foxhole friends. I dedicate this book to your support.

I singled out a few others in the book, like Brian Humphrey who is paralyzed and bedridden. He has such a burden in his heart that he prays for me when I visit and just lives every day with the hope he will be able to stand up again someday. I am so humbled by his concern. Every time I visit Brian, I feel so inspired when I leave. I love you, Brian. Keep hope alive my friend.

To Roger and Jan Adams, who have been close friends for over 50 years, I could not ask for more loyal friends. If I was ever in need of anything, they would drop anything they are doing and come to my assistance. Losing a daughter, who was serving God in Africa and was killed in a car accident, is so heart wrenching. I was by their side for several days after the terrible news arrived. How they kept their faith during unimaginable grief was such a great example that gave me strength to continue my journey one step at a time. Never give up. This time will pass someday.

The Whitaker Clan

To my family, including Rick and Cathy and their kids' families, you are the reason I am here today and writing a book about my journey. Not only were you with me every hour of every day, but you inspired me, your dad, PaPa, brother and Uncle, to pass along the lessons to you no matter the size of the obstacle and the difficulty. With God holding your right hand, you can conquer anything on your way to success. Remember the bigger the obstacle, the bigger the reward and the satisfaction that you overcame and came out a better person.

To Larry and Suzi Byrd. You have struggled with cancer and other serious health issues for the last several years. If I needed to know what to expect and how I can do this, all I had to do was give them a call. They were always checking in on me to ensure I was ok. I cannot imagine how they continue to fight each challenge with such great and mighty faith in God to deliver them. He did that so many times, over and over. However, while I was writing this book, my childhood friend and high school and college sports teammate, Larry passed away and is now walking the golden streets of heaven. His wife, Suzi still checks in on me to make sure I am ok, but I am sure she misses Larry every day.

His passing left a big hole in my heart. He still inspires me to continue to live with a passion for helping others in need.

During one of my first chemo treatments, my daughter Cathleen was sitting with me. She said, "Dad, I know you love Yellowstone, so let's plan a trip for next year, July 2023." As a child growing up, our parents took Rick and me to Yellowstone several times when the summer baseball season was over. Back then, we camped out in tents and watched the bears roam the campgrounds looking for easy food to devour. It was an amazing time of our lives. I have always wanted to take my kids and grandkids to Yellowstone. I had over 12 chemo treatments, the Whipple surgery, and months of recovery before I could say I made it well enough to survive and travel again. But, we planned the trip anyway and made our reservations a year in advance. That was one of my biggest motivators as I faced all the huge challenges ahead of me.

Cal, Teddy, Cathleen, Me and Georgie

In July 2023, just as we planned, I loaded up the RV with Cathleen, Cal, Georgie, and Teddy and we went to Yellowstone for a two-week trip. It was one of the most satisfying trips I have ever taken. Not only had I fought through the tough days of fighting cancer and all the side effects, but I was also able to live my dream again. I really didn't think it would be possible.

So, now I have had two CT scans that showed no signs of cancer. I still have a long way to go before I can ring the bell of being cancer free. If my scans continue to show no signs of cancer, I hope to ring the bell somewhere after year two or three.

On two separate occasions while getting my chemotherapy treatments I have heard the bell ring for two cancer survivors. Throughout both floors people stop what they are doing, and you could hear them clapping with joy that someone else is ringing the bell and declared cancer free. Patients and staff are so excited and happy for them. Hearing that sound brings a tear to your eye and a lump in your throat that just maybe someday that could be you.

I can only imagine what ringing the bell would mean to me. It would mean this journey had reached the end of the path. It would mean that if you have one out left in the game, you can still win. It would mean that despite the long odds of survival you are going to beat them and declare with a loud voice, "I am not a statistic!"

The goal of a cancer survivor is to "ring the bell"

Most importantly, it would mean that the power of prayer and the support from so many foxhole friends can heal anyone. Even just an ordinary guy like me.

Place your ribbon of hope on the wall

Ringing the bell would prove that despite the dark clouds, the sun can still shine through and brighten the sky. If we have hope in our lives and let it into our souls and drive us to never give up, we can overcome the difficulties in our lives.

Believe in yourself, keep the faith, trust someone to be your friend and accept their help. Let God hold your right hand and lead the way.

Let Hope In....Whit

Believe in Hope

For prayer support or just want to discuss your journey, contact me at rgwhit1@gmail.com